THE MARLBOROUGH DOCTORS

Six Generations of One Family's
Medical Practice
since 1792

THE MARLBOROUGH DOCTORS

*Six Generations of One Family's
Medical Practice
since 1792*

BY

DICK MAURICE

AND

Chapter Five: Part One

BY

TIM MAURICE

ALAN SUTTON PUBLISHING LIMITED

First published in the United Kingdom in 1994 by
Alan Sutton Publishing Ltd
Phoenix Mill · Far Thrupp · Stroud · Gloucestershire

First published in the United States of America in 1994 by
Alan Sutton Publishing Inc · 83 Washington Street · Dover NH 03820

British Library Cataloguing in Publication Data
A catalogue record for this book is available from the British Library.

ISBN 0-07509-0831-9

Library of Congress Cataloging in Publication Data applied for.

Typesetting and origination by
Alan Sutton Publishing Limited.
Printed and bound in Great Britain
By Hartnolls, Bodmin, Cornwall.

Contents

List of Illustrations

Acknowledgements

First, my brother Tim, who had many of the documents that I have used, who helped me with some of the editing and who has contributed one chapter on his experiences in the practice. I am greatly indebted to the late Mr Clifford Currie and to Dr Stephen Lock. They both found numerous errors in my spelling, grammar and punctuation; I hope these have now been corrected. My son, David Pierce, named after his great great grandfather, has helped me in writing the Epilogue.

Dr Irvine Loudon's book – *Medical Care and the General Practitioner 1750–1850* published by the Clarendon Press, Oxford – has been a useful source of information on the development of general practice over the first sixty years of the Maurice practice. Dr Loudon has also supplied me with a number of facts about my ancestors that I did not know. Although some of the material concerning the Maurices that appears in Professor Richard Lovell's biography of Lord Moran – *Churchill's Doctor* published by the Royal Society of Medicine Services Limited was supplied by me it was only on reading the book I learned that Lord Moran, as a young man, had thoughts of becoming the resident medical officer to Marlborough College.

I am also indebted to Mr David West, archivist to Marlborough College, to Mr Alan Rix, to Pamela Colman, Mrs McCubbin, and to the Wiltshire Record Office for allowing me to read certain papers. Lastly I am deeply indebted to the long since deceased Miss Ada Kindersley, first cousin of my father. It must have been some time in the 1940s that she gave me her 1911 *Encyclopaedia Britannica*. It has supplied me with invaluable information both about developments in medicine, many of those mentioned in the book, and such diverse facts as the introduction of the telephone and the motor car.

Prologue

Thelwall Maurice, the founder of the family practice, was born in 1767 – the elder son of Thomas Maurice and Jane *née* Pierce. The Maurice family can trace their ancestors back to the ninth century and some would argue much further. The family had always lived in North Wales and their principal abode was Lloran Ucha (Upper Lloran), which at one time had comprised a very large estate. They regularly married into the Welsh aristocracy but the Welsh did not adopt surnames until the end of the sixteenth century. Thus Thelwall's great great great great great grandfather was Morus ap (son of) Maredudd of Lloran Ucha. His sons all took the surname Maurice, and Thelwall was a descendant of his second son, David. David's son, Edward, was Thelwall's great great great grandfather; he was High Sheriff of Denbighshire in 1638 and Montgomery in 1640. The family did distinguish themselves in other ways; notably Thomas Maurice, Thelwall's second cousin once removed. He was a great scholar and author of a classic work *Indian Antiquities* which he dedicated to the University of Oxford.

Thelwall spent his early life in a house which his father and grandfather shared at Plas Enion, near Ruthin – his father's uncle had inherited Lloran Ucha. Plas Enion is a large and beautiful farmhouse of the late fifteenth or early sixteenth century. Thelwall's mother died in April 1780 at the age of thirty-three, leaving him without a mother at the age of thirteen together with his younger brother, Thomas, who was only eight. Thelwall's father remarried and it was after this that he decided to leave Wales and to study medicine at St Thomas's Hospital. Medicine was a new vocation for a Maurice. He achieved an M.D., most probably by purchase from a Scottish university; this was a common practice at the time and a doctorate could be obtained by recommendation of two members of the staff at St Thomas's without ever attending the University. It was in 1792, at the age of twenty-five, that he joined Dr Pinckney in practice in Marlborough.

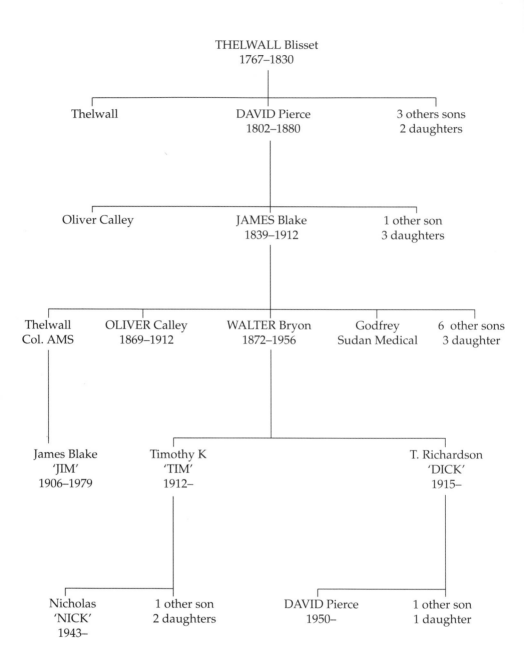

MAURICE FAMILY TREE

All those named were doctors; those in capitals were partners in the practice, although Walter's brothers, Thelwall and Godfrey, both were at one time assistants in the practice

CHAPTER 1

Thelwall and the First Generation

The reason for Thelwall Maurice's decision to join Dr Pinckney in practice in Marlborough and not return to Wales can only be speculation; it is possible he did not get on with his step-mother, who is said to have been his father's 'housekeeper'. He might have learned of a suitable vacancy for a surgeon apothecary in Marlborough from the authorities at St Thomas's Hospital: St Thomas's at that time held the Lordship of the Manor of Pewsey, only seven miles from Marlborough. Another possibility is that he knew of the vacancy through family connections. Reference to the Day Books, two of which survive from these early years, shows that medicines were frequently prescribed for a Mrs D. Maurice, and occasionally for a Mr Maurice whose occupation was recorded as 'Draper'. These Maurices do not appear on any family tree but may well have been distant cousins. Mr Maurice is also known to have been a parchment maker and was a prominent citizen of the Borough. It may be that he was responsible for making the shrouds for burying the dead and it was this that led to the apocryphal story handed down through the generations that two Maurice brothers had originally settled in Marlborough in partnership – one as the doctor, the other as the undertaker.

Hospital training, such as that undertaken by Thelwall, was only becoming at all common at the end of the eighteenth century. Dr Pinckney had learned his medicine by being apprenticed to another surgeon apothecary. Surgeon apothecaries came from a fairly broad social range, but Dr Pinckney came from much the same background as Thelwall. The Pinckneys had originally come over with William the Conqueror from Picguini in Picardy. They had been associated with Wiltshire for many centuries and were small country gentry in the reign of Elizabeth I. Some of the family lived at Wolfhall, near Burbage and not far from Marlborough, for many generations. By a strange coincidence they also had Welsh ancestry, as Pinckneys had three times married Tripps. The Tripps had Owen ancestors and they have been traced back to Hwfa ap Gwynedd – believed to have been the founder of the first of the fifteen Noble Tribes of Gwynedd. The

1

Maurices are descended from Mereddyd ap Bleddyn – Prince of Powys and Head of the third of the fifteen tribes of North Wales. However, it is highly unlikely that Thelwall Maurice and Robert Pinckney knew anything of this!

Robert Pinckney had been bound as an apprentice to Thomas Warner, County Surgeon & Apothecary of Marlborough, in 1769. His indentures state:-

> His Secrets keep, his lawful commands everywhere gladly do, he shall do no damage to his said Master nor see it be done for others.... The goods of his said Master he shall not waste nor the same without Licence of him to any give or lend. Taverns, Inns & Almshouses shall he not haunt. At cards, Dice, Tables or any other unlawful Game he shall not play. Nor from the service of his said Master Day nor Night absent himself, but in all things as an honest and Faithful Apprentice shall and will demean himself toward his said Master and all his during the said Term.
>
> And the said Thomas Warner for and consideration of the sum of £105 to him now in hand paid by the same William Pinckney doth hereby acknowledge the said apprentice in the art of Surgeon and Apothecary which he now useth shall teach and instruct, the best Way and Manner that he can, finding and allowing unto his said apprentice sufficient Meat, Drink, Lodging and all other Necessaries during the said Term.
>
> 12 August 1769

It may well be that Thelwall's decision to join Dr Pinckney in Marlborough was influenced by the possibilities it offered for a satisfactory life as a medical man. Marlborough is an ancient Borough – its first charter was granted in 1204. Wiltshire is a large county, but the central part comprising Salisbury Plain is only sparsely populated – the urban areas are situated on the periphery of the county boundaries. Marlborough is on the northern and eastern part of the county and has around it the Marlborough Downs, Savernake Forest, the Pewsey Vale and the Kennet Valley. Agriculture was the principal industry and there were a number of large estates in the area which should assure a reasonable income for a surgeon apothecary. At all events he decided to join Dr Pinckney, and his descendants seem to have agreed with this decision since they have remained in practice in Marlborough without a break ever since, and should go on for some time yet.

How the practice worked in those early days must to some extent be a matter for conjecture, but fortunately there are some records – notably two Day Books – the first from Saturday, 1 November 1794 to Thursday, 21 January 1796 – the second from Sunday, 17 November

1799 to Friday, 6 March 1801. The dates, the journeys (iters) made and the prescriptions are all entered in Latin – a practice that was still in operation some 154 years later at the start of the National Health Service. There were other surgeons and apothecaries in the area, even in Marlborough itself, but the most striking feature of these Day Books is the immense area covered by the Pinckney Maurice practice. The distances travelled were far greater than today – and this was a hundred years before the motor car began to come into use. Patients could be seen and prescribed for over distances of at least 10 miles in every direction – some from even further, notably in the Swindon area. Fifty years before the advent of the railways Swindon was little more than a village, although the Marlborough practice is believed at some stage to have had a branch surgery there. Marlborough was a much more important centre: it was on the main route from London to Bath; travellers in the stage coaches would stop overnight in the famous Castle Inn, once the home of the Seymours, the dukes of Somerset, and now part of Marlborough College. Some patients are recorded as living in Devizes – 13 miles to the west – others in Hungerford – 10 miles east and many from villages far to the south of Marlborough.

The Day Books record the name of the patient and the various medicines, lotions, drafts, powders and pills prescribed. These medicaments were the main source of income for the apothecary surgeons in the eighteenth and much of the nineteenth century; they were handed out in small amounts each time and the next day might be repeated or some new preparation would be substituted. Often two or more medicaments would be prescribed at a time; the doctor's income depended on this, but it would seem patients were just as addicted to taking medicaments in the eighteenth century as they are today, although few can have done them much good. No doubt faith does play a big part in recovery. Occasionally a patient would pay at the time of receiving their medicine, this would be recorded in the Day Book and it would appear that one shilling would be the usual price for a single substance, this would be over £2 by today's standards. Three medicaments that are recorded in these early Day Books would have been of real value – opium, whose principal component is morphine, for the relief of pain; digitalis, from the leaves of foxgloves and already known to be of value in treating dropsy; and iron for anaemia.

One document which has somehow survived the passing of generations is a well-printed paper by Thomas Beddoes.

A PROPOSAL TOWARDS THE IMPROVEMENT OF MEDICINE

It deals with the subject of 'pneumatic medicine' and the 'application of elastic fluid' to the cure of diseases. Unfortunately the paper does not state what pneumatic medicine and elastic fluid were. The paper is by Thomas Beddoes M.D. of the Mall, Clifton, Bristol and dated 29 September 1794. It states that these treatments have been used with success abroad and to have 'exceeded rather than disappointed expectation' and to have had some success with animals. The purpose of the paper was to raise money to found an institution which 'should be conducted with a view to the attainment of two objects 1. to ascertain the effects of the powerful agents in various diseases, and 2. to discover the best method of procuring and applying them.'

Dr Beddoes suggests that three or four thousand pounds should be sufficient to start the institution. He wrote a personal note on the parchment on which the paper is printed and addressed to : 'Mr Maurice – Surgeon – One Street – Marlborough.' The address and the note is written in Thomas Beddoes's own hand and reads:-

> I venture to send you one of these proposals wishing you may think it worth recommending – We have succeeding in disarming cancer of all its terror and I hope all its danger. I would undertake to remove all the pain of the worst cancer and would hope to cure it. Our power is, I firmly believe, adequate to the cure of consumption – the application is difficult, perhaps impracticable, without rooms of modified air – you need not be anxious to return a speedy answer – I am sir, yours, T. Beddoes.

The end of the printed document reads as follows:-

Speedily to be published
A familiar explanation of the principles on which benefit may be
expected from
breathing elastic fluids in various diseases, by
T H O M A S   B E D D O E S   M. D.
to which will be added
A description and drawing of a simple domestic apparatus for procuring
and inhaling certain elastic fluids, by
J A M E S   W A T T   Esq.
OF HEATHFIELD, NEAR BIRMINGHAM.

It must say something of Thelwall's early success at Marlborough that Thomas Beddoes knew of him and sought his help within two years of his joining the practice. Thomas Beddoes (1760–1808) was a physician and scientific writer of international renown. The 'Pneumatic Institution' was founded but the original aim was gradually reduced and it became an ordinary sick hospital.

The word 'Attendans' hardly ever appears in these early Day Books. Many patients must have attended the surgery in person. During Thelwall's time it was situated on the North side of the high street and close to the Town Hall. It would appear that patients living locally would be charged only for their treatment and not for the visit. Often someone is recorded as living many miles away and receiving various medicaments but no visit is made. Presumably if they were unable to attend they sent a relative or servant bearing a note describing their trouble and would be issued with something appropriate. If a charge was made for a local visit one shilling appears to have been the normal rate, but the more wealthy – such as visitors to the Castle Inn – might be faced with larger bills. A Mrs Stratton staying at the Castle Inn over two days in November 1794 was given a number of different substances; a note against her name states that she paid £1 11s and a further 11s was to be posted.

Other entries sometimes recorded in the Day Books refer to the occupation of the patients – maltster, bricklayer, sadler, blacksmith etc. On occasion it would be the maid or servant of the name recorded. Many local clergy figure among their patients, and sometimes surgeon appears against the name – very likely no charge would be made in either case.

The writing is old-fashioned but it is possible after all this time to know which entries were made by Robert Pinckney and which are in Thelwall's hand. Wolfhall, near Burbage, and some 6 miles from Marlborough on the other side of Savernake Forest, was a Pinckney residence for many years; Robert Pinckney's brother lived there in 1794 and there were other Pinckneys in the district who apparently lived 'at the Bank'. Entries in the 1794/95 Day Book relating to visits or medicaments for the Pinckneys are clearly written by Robert; they would hardly be likely to trust that new young man, Thelwall Maurice. Entries relating to the Maurices, the 'Draper' and his family, were entered in the other hand, and no doubt were written by Thelwall. These handwritten entries show that even at this early stage Thelwall had acquired the Calley family of Overtown, near Swindon, as his patients, a connection that was to continue through many generations; in due course three of his children were to marry three Calley grandchildren. Thelwall had married a local girl two years after coming to Marlborough and he lost no time in starting a family.

These early Day Books give some sort of picture of the way in which the practice was organised; they certainly show that Drs Pinckney and Maurice carried a very heavy work load. Between them they managed a full seven day week, and the handwriting shows that it was rare for either partner to have a whole day off, not even on Sundays. Opening the Day Book *Dei Saturni* 22 November 1794 we find that some twenty-two medicaments were dispensed for twelve patients. The only remotely surgical procedures recorded that day are for Mr Hillier – 'Dressing his head – 1/-'– this is in Thelwall's handwriting, while Dr Pinckney 'dressed a wound on Ben Heath's boy'. Dr Pinckney seems to have made all the distant visits (iters) made that day. He saw Mr Willes at Rockley – 1 mile north of Marlborough – Mr Swaite at Wilton – some 7 miles to the south – to another Mr Swaite at Bacons Farm and Richard Andrew's daughter at Nag's Head. On *Die Solis* 23 November no fewer than twenty-five substances were dispensed. Thelwall had to visit Mrs Rendall at Oxenwood, which would have meant a ride of some twenty-four miles there and back. Dr Pinckney visited both the Swaites again and a Thomas Stockwell at Baydon some 8 miles north-east of Marlborough. On *Die Lunae* 24 November thirty-five medicaments were handed out to twenty-four patients. Thelwall visited Mr Bennett at Ogbourne – 4 miles north, and Mr Amiss – 4 miles south on the other side of Savernake Forest. This visit was made in the evening after he had reduced a fractured arm – 'Reduct: Fract: Brachii' – on Isaac Ralph. Among those receiving medicines that day were Mrs Calley, who had Glauber's salt, and Mrs D. Maurice, who was given *vin ipecac*. Dr Pinckney had to visit Thomas Stockwell again at Baydon and the Kingstone family at Little Bedwyn seven miles in the opposite direction.

With such large distances to cover it is hardly surprising that Pinckney and Maurice were soon looking for more help in the practice, particularly to dispense the medicines and other medicaments. On 26 October 1795 an advertisement appeared in the *Salisbury & Winchester Journal*: 'Wanted – an APPRENTICE to a SURGEON and APOTHECARY in full practice – apply to Messrs Pinckney and Maurice – Marlborough – Wilts.'

Although designated surgeon apothecaries, the Day Books show that surgery played little part in their everyday work. In the days before anaesthesia it was only a matter of treating injuries to limbs, attending to wounds, draining abscesses and extracting teeth. For example, in the month of January 1795 one dental extraction is recorded, one dislocated shoulder was reduced and a fractured collar bone was treated. Two abscesses were drained and dressings were applied on six occasions.

The practice of midwifery by surgeon apothecaries had become increasingly common in the second half of the eighteenth century. Both Thelwall and Pinckney attended a number of deliveries, no doubt on occasion being summoned by the midwife when there were complications. In the month of January 1795 four deliveries are recorded, two of them some 7 miles from Marlborough. The doctors were sometimes paid at the time of delivery and one guinea seems to have been the normal rate, but on occasion smaller sums would be charged. Haust or mist anodyne is always recorded as being given to the mother at the time of delivery – it was indeed the standard treatment for pain.

On 5 September 1800 an entry in the Day Book for that year shows that Thelwall reduced a fractured thigh bone on Mrs Calley at Overtown, a procedure which no doubt was preceeded by bleeding in order to reduce the level of consciousness. He then had to make the long ride over the Downs daily for some days with fresh bottles of haust anodyne before being able to reduce his visits to every fourth or fifth day. Perhaps it was his successful handling of her case that was to lead to the friendship between his children and Mrs Calley's grandchildren.

Bleeding prior to surgical procedures could be carried to extreme. In 1929 Mr Howard Cunnington, Hon. Curator of the Wiltshire Archaeological Society, wrote a book which included some early eighteenth- and nineteenth-century inquests. On 18 December 1805 an inquest was held on Thomas Paisey, who had been thrown from the box of a stage coach in which he was travelling as a pasenger. The coach overturned close to the Marlborough Town Hall as it was passing a waggon. One of the four horses shied, the coach ran up the steps of the Town Hall and the unfortunate Thomas Paisey fell under the wheels of the waggon. The rear wheel pinioned his chest and the waggon had to be backed off. Thelwall lived nearby and was called to find the poor man in the arms of some people carrying him to the Bear and Castle Inn. Thelwall at once attempted to bleed him but failed; he died 10 minutes later.

Robert Pinckney died in 1809. There would certainly have been at least one other additional surgeon apothecary in the practice at this time but there are no records of this.

Family group painted by Wainwright in 1838.

This picture can be no better described than by the words found on the label affixed to the back of the frame by Tim:

David Pierce Maurice, my great-grandfather and third son of Thelwall Maurice, founder of the family practice, kneels. His wife, Marianne, reclines on the couch. She was the daughter of Henry Bullock by his wife, Arabella née Calley, of Burderop Park. The dress that she is wearing is in my possession. One of Marianne's sisters, Louisa, stands at the head of the couch. Between her parents is Adelaide, David and Marianne's eldest daughter. She married the Rev. H. Pix and I can remember their daughter, Julia. The picture was painted in the drawing room at Lloran House.

Thelwall seems to have acquired quite a flourishing practice among the local squires and landowners. There were several large estates in the area which passed from generation to generation in the same family; the Calleys of Overtown and Burderop Park, the Goddards of Clyffe Pypard and the Burdetts of Ramsbury Manor were cared for by succeeding Maurices through five and sometimes six generations. Not a great deal is known about Thelwall's income but it appears to have been higher than that of the average surgeon apothecary of the day. A country doctor who earned £1,000 a year would be exceptional, but it would appear that Thelwall must have earned at least that.

Some time in the early 1930s the then Sir Francis Burdett found an account among his papers that had been submitted by Thelwall to his ancestor – also Sir Francis Burdett (1770–1844). The Burdetts were baronets and he had been the radical M.P. for Westminster for thirty years. The account dates from 16 October 1814 to 2 April 1815 and every item is entered. They relate almost entirely to Lady Burdett who was clearly suffering from a very grave illness. Visits were frequently made daily and charged 10s 6d – the daily medicines and powders prescribed vary in price from 4s to 1s 6d. The total bill for these visits and medicaments amounted to £107 6s. But that was not all. She had required night attendance for sixty nights, for which she was charged £63. Originally he seems to have asked for £126 but the final bill for night attendance was halved. Finally Thelwall had to escort her Ladyship to London for which he charged £20 and a further £7 1s for the hire of a chaise to take them there. A note at the end of the bill from Thelwall states 'Lady Burdett gave Mr Maurice £100 for his night attendance and for his time in accompanying her Ladyship to Town. Sir Francis paid Mr Maurice's expenses in returning to Marlborough. Therefore only £107 6s to pay.' On the reverse side of the bill there is a further note. This is in a different hand, probably that of Sir Francis:-

Bill	107.6.0
Nightly attendance	63.0.0
Attendance in London	20.0.0
Chaise hire	7.1.0
	100.0.0
£	97.7.0

The £100 had already been paid by Lady Burdett; it would appear Thelwall had got his sums wrong. The bill was given to Walter Maurice of the fourth generation; he was quick to point out the bill had not been receipted.

Astley Cooper (1768–1825) was a noted surgeon of the early nineteenth century. Although a few months younger than Thelwall he had been appointed an Anatomy Demonstrator at St Thomas's Hospital in 1789, and became a lecturer there in 1791. This would have brought him into contact with Thelwall when he too was learning his anatomy and surgery at the hospital. In 1824 the fourth edition of *A TREATISE on DISLOCATIONS and FRACTURES* by Sir Astley Cooper Bart, FRS, Surgeon to the King, etc. was published. The book recorded a number of letters sent to Sir Astley giving personal experiences in treating dislocations and fractures.

CASE XV

Marlborough, Feb. 12, 1823.

Sir,

Permit me to send you the following case of dislocation of the thigh bone on the dorsum of the ileum.

George Davies, aged thirty five, on the first day of the present month, in descending a flight of steps at a mill in this neighbourhood, with a sack of wheat on his back, missed a step or two and, in endeavouring to regain his footing, the whole weight of the load fell upon him and the violence of the shock bore him down several steps lower, where he lay totally incapable of further motion until assistance was procured.

He was then conveyed to the adjoining village. On examination, the limb was found considerably shorter than its fellow, the foot turned inwards and resting on the tarsus of the other leg. The head of the bone was distinctly felt, lodged among the glutei muscles. All the other symptoms were unequivocal. In about three hours after the occurrence of the accident, due preparation having been made, thirty ounces of blood were taken from the arm, the pullies were adjusted according to your directions and, gradual extension being made, the head of the bone was eventually brought on a line with the acetabulum. A towel was now passed under the thigh, by which means the bone was elevated and suddenly, with an audible snap, it slipped into its proper cavity. The man is going on well, but he is still suffering from the effect of the contusion and has not been allowed to make use of the limb.

I am, Sir,

Your's respectfully,

T. MAURICE.

P.S. The reduction was accomplished in about ten minutes.

Earlier in the book Sir Astley had written:- 'The constitutional means to be employed for the purpose of reduction are those which produce a tendency to syncope and this necessary state may best be induced by one or other of the following means, viz. bleeding, warm bath and nausea. Of these remedies I consider bleeding the most powerful and, that the effect may be produced as quickly as possible, the blood should be withdrawn from a large orifice and the patient kept in an erect position for, by this mode of depletion, syncope is produced before too large a quantity of blood is lost.'

The most prominent local landowning family of all was not cared for by the Pinckney Maurice practice – this was the Brudenell Bruces – first earls – then in 1821 created marquesses of Ailesbury. They owned huge estates to the south of Marlborough including Savernake Forest. They were Tories and it is possible that Thelwall was a Whig which would account for his being medical attendant to the Burdetts but not the Ailesbury family. In the early nineteenth century the Marquess employed Mr Washbourne and then Mr John Gardiner. 'Mr John Gardiner is an apothecary. He dropped into the town, and having bought the business of Mr Washbourne, who was Lord Ailesbury's medical attendant, he by that means purchased his Lordship for a patient, and a Corporationship for himself.' ('Tory politics, 1835' reproduced in *Marlborough Town & Countryside* by E.G.H. Kempson and G.W. Murray, Whittington Press). It was David, Thelwall's third son, who was to take over the care of the Brudenell Bruces. The fifth marquess gained his title on the death of his nephew; he had married Georgiana Pinckney, granddaughter of Robert's brother, who had lived at Wolfhall.

One public post that Thelwall held was that of medical officer to the Grammar School. This was no sinecure post; he was 'constantly in the habit of attending the school as a medical man'. The Revd James Lawes, who had been educated at Winchester and Oxford, was appointed headmaster in 1809. The Grammar School at this time had boarders and day boys. The reason for Thelwall's frequent attendance was the appalling brutality the headmaster meted out to his pupils.

A.R. Stedman, in his book *Marlborough and the Upper Kennet Country*, enlarges on this: 'One boy, Clift, was beaten the whole way down his back most cruelly, another, Reilly, received a blow on the side of his head, causing blood to flow over his exercise books.' Other cases are listed but perhaps the worst is Courtney Boyle Brice who entered the school in 1810. Two years later, when only twelve years old, he 'complained of pain in the side of the head, and a weakness of his eyes . . .' He had received 'a blow with a dictionary from Mr

Lawes . . .' Mr Maurice applied 'leeches to both temples.' Two years later the unfortunate boy was beaten badly about the head and face by a rod and then Mr Lawes 'raising his hand, with his fist clenched, struck the boy a violent blow upon his head, which made him insensible at the time. Six weeks later the boy suffered from constipation, relieved by large doses of quicksilver; from fainting fits; from a tumour, dispersed by leeches; and from epileptic fits, during which it took four men to hold him down.'

Thelwall's success as a medical man can to some extent be gauged by the careers of his children and the families into which they married. The eldest son was also named Thelwall and was born in 1795. He decided to pursue a medical career like his father, to whom he was apprenticed as an apothecary before continuing his training at St Thomas's Hospital. Apprentices had to accept a great deal of reponsibility as records of inquests held in the Borough of Marlborough in the late eighteenth and early nineteenth century show. On 15 June 1811 young Thelwall, only 16 years of age, was summoned at about 5 a.m. to a boy of about 7 who had been run over by a wagon. Thelwall annointed his belly, which was bruised and gave him medicine but he died about 9 a.m. Another witness stated that Mr Maurice 'annointed his bowells.'

The first half of the nineteenth century was a time of upheaval in the medical world. The physicians were bitterly opposed to the apothecaries whom they regarded as little more than tradesmen. However, in 1815 the Apothecaries Act was passed, introducing an examination for the Society of Apothecaries, but this was not retrospective; those in practice before 1815 could continue in practice. Nor was the act rigidly enforced, and only in 1858 did the passing of the Medical Act finally abolish the right of medical practitioners to qualify simply by serving as apprentices. A further clause in the Apothecaries Act of 1815 made it compulsory to pass an examination for the M.R.C.S. in order to practise as a surgeon apothecary. Young Thelwall duly qualified as M.R.C.S., L.S.A. (Licentiate Society of Apothecaries) in 1816. Presumably his father did not need help in the Marlborough practice at this time as he moved to Reading and lived at 96 London Street. He became consultant surgeon to the Royal Berkshire Hospital, was surgeon to the police and the Bluecoat School and obtained his Fellowship of the Royal College of Surgeons in 1844. He was the first of Thelwall's children to marry into the Bullock family. He married in 1819 and his wife, Bessie, was the daughter of Henry and Arabella

Bullock of Stoneham Parva and Grosvenor Place, Bath. Arabella Bullock was the elder daughter of Mrs Calley of Overtown House. Her brother had inherited Burderop Park after the death of his father in 1791 and was M.P. for Cricklade.

John, Thelwall's second son, entered the Church and became Rector of Michaelmarsh in Hampshire. A graduate of Brasenose College, Oxford, he married the Hon. Jane Powys, daughter of the second Lord Lilford in 1836 at the age of 37. They were to have a son, grandson, great grandson and great, great grandson in direct descent entering the Church; it would appear the Maurices rather tend to follow in fathers' footsteps.

His fourth son was Thomas Maurice, he too entered the Church and was Rector of Harnhill in Gloucestershire for forty-one years. He married Harriet, daughter and heiress of John Sherwood of Castle Hill, Reading. After her death he married Jane Martha, elder daughter of William Croome of North Cerney House, Gloucestershire.

The fifth son, James, was a lawyer. After the death of his uncle he returned to Wales in 1838 to live with his aunt by marriage at Ruthin in Denbighshire. At the age of 44 he qualified as a barrister and was called to the Bar in 1853. He became Deputy Lieutenant for the County of Denbigh. He was Mayor of Ruthin for four successive years.

Thelwall and Anne had five daughters; the first died when only one year old and the second when only aged twenty-one. Ellinor, the third daughter, married Tom Bullock, her brother's brother-in-law. Jane Pierce married G. Pilcher, lecturer in surgery and President of the Medical Society of London. The youngest, Martha, married R.D. Grainger, who was to become a Fellow of the Royal Society and a member of the Council of the Royal College of Surgeons.

It was David Pierce, Thelwall's third son, who joined his father in the practice about the year 1827, thus ensuring a continuation of the line in Marlborough. Thelwall died on 17 February 1830 aged sixty-two, and there is a memorial tablet to him and to his wife and two daughters in the side chapel of St Peter's church.

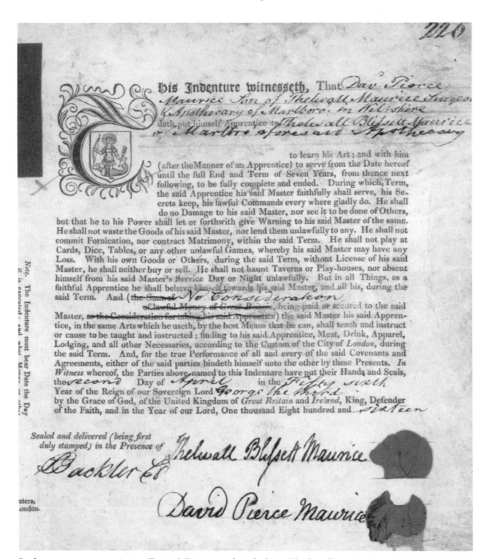

Indenture, apprenticing David Pierce to his father, Thelwall

CHAPTER 2

David Pierce and the Second Generation

David Pierce was born on 5 March 1802. After education at the Grammar School he was apprenticed to his father when only fourteen. His printed indentures, still in existence, are worded almost identically to those of Robert Pinckney to Thomas Warner except that they also state he is not to commit fornication or contract matrimony! 'The sum of' is crossed out and 'no consideration' inked in. His indentures bound him to his father for seven years, but probably at the age of eighteen he was released to study medicine at St Thomas's and so gained his Licentiate of the Society of Apothecaries in 1821 when only nineteen. His father's teaching must take the credit for his gaining his L.S.A. at such a young age. In 1825 he gained his Membership of the Royal College of Surgeons. Much later, in 1852, he was to become a Fellow of the Royal College of Surgeons. After leaving St Thomas's he worked at Guy's Hospital and then in Paris. He joined his father at the age of twenty-five and so had some three years to learn the ropes before his father's death. In 1829 he was the last Maurice to marry a Bullock; this was Marianne.

The Maurices appear to have been on good terms with the local community, among them the Hancocks, who had owned the bank at 42 High Street, and the Baskervilles who, had extensive property including Poulton House. John Hancock had died in 1818 when his only child, Anne, was rising twenty-one. She inherited the Hancock property and a considerable fortune and then married Thomas Baskerville. Soon after his marriage in 1829 David was allowed to rent the old bank in perpetuity at a nominal rent, he called it Lloran House after the ancestral home in North Wales; with considerable extensions it was to remain the family home until the 1950s. The house contained a large safe, which had been in use when it was a bank, and some papers were still in it when David acquired the property, among them the deeds of Littlecote to the Popham family in the reign of Queen Anne. Regrettably, they were not returned to their

15

David Pierce (1802–1880)

owners until 1990 when they were handed to a Popham descendant who had herself been born in Littlecote.

The early Maurices tended to have large families; Marianne bore David three sons and three daughters over the first ten years of their married life. Their third son, James Blake, who was destined to continue the line in Marlborough, was born on 22 October 1839 and poor Marianne, perhaps worn out by so many pregnancies, possibly suffering from tuberculosis, died on 25 June 1840 when only thirty-one.

David's assistant in the practice was Dr John Maule. Among the family papers there is a letter from him to David dated 22 October 1839. Apparently on the previous day David was carrying out an operation on someone's skull in a house in the High Street close to Lloran House. This must have been unusual in the days before anaesthesia, presumably the patient was in coma after sustaining a fracture. Dr Maule was assisting and on three occasions had been rounded on by David and told not to put his fingers on the bone when David was handling it himself, and that in front of all the people present. Dr Maule was so upset that he had walked out. Marianne's diary records that he was a frequent visitor to dine at Lloran House; after this incident he did not start to dine there again until 7 November, by which time the trouble had evidently been resolved.

The journeys (iters) made are to the same villages as in his father's time, with many of the old names still appearing such as the Merrimans and the Hancocks. Even allowing for the different pens being used, the handwriting show that three persons were making the entries. With the immense distances that had to be covered a patient would often be visited by different members of the practice for the same illness. One family that figures in this Day Book is that of the Browns of West Street Auburn – now known as Aldbourne. They have farmed the same area for many generations and it is claimed that five generations of Browns have been brought into the world by five generations of Maurices.

The Baskervilles owned all the land separating The Old Bank House, now Lloran House, from Figgins Lane and running down to the Kennet. Even so, David was able to establish his surgery in one of the cottages owned by the Baskervilles at the top of Figgins Lane. The whole of this property was eventually acquired by his son, James. As in Thelwall's time there was no let up on Sundays. On 10 August 1845 seventeen patients were treated. These included visits made, (the entries being almost certainly in David's hand), to Chiseldon, Wroughton, Ufcott, Berwick, Monkton and Beckhampton, a round trip of the best part of 20 miles. On these long journeys a groom would be sent out with a fresh horse by a direct route over the downs to meet David at a half-way point. Villagers on the route knew of these long rounds and if they lived on the way would hang out a piece of cloth if they required the doctor's services. Those living off the road would ask a neighbour to perform this service and so get the doctor to visit.

One family figures with great frequency in the Day Book 1844–46; the Codringtons of Wroughton House, and particularly Mrs Laeticia Codrington. David or his assistant visited her regularly in the first eight months of 1845 and on 10 September an entry is recorded '*Iter et attendans* at London *die* 8th and 9th Sept.' By 11 September she was being attended again at Wroughton. She required several more visits over the next two weeks and then from 27 September to 7 November she was visited on a daily basis – 16 miles there and back – and received some thirty-five medicaments. It is sad that the medicines give no sort of clue as to the nature of her illness. After this the visits became less frequent. Her tomb at Wroughton records that she died on 28 November 1845. Six years after her death one of David's daughters married Thomas Codrington, her nephew by marriage.

The local landowning families that figure so largely in the Day Book must have contributed greatly to the size of David's income. He was fortunate that he was able to succeed his father and take over his practice; something which has helped succeeding generations of Maurices ever since. There is no record how much David earned, but to judge by what he was to achieve in extending his property, it must have been more than the average income of a country doctor in the first half of the 19th century. There was a large increase in the number of practitioners during the first half of the century and this led to increasing competition; many earned only £200 or even less in a year, more than £1,000 would still be exceptional. However there may have been other factors at work. Not long after the death of his wife, Marianne, he married again. His second wife was Rebecca, widow of John Withers Clark of Preshute and daughter of John Hooper of North Stoke Manor, Somerset. Whereas Marianne is not believed to have had a large inheritance, Rebecca, who had no children, would appear to have owned property around Preshute and Manton on the outskirts of Marlborough. She did not have any children by David and this property was of considerable value both to David and to his descendants in the future. Certainly the marriage appears to have been a success.

During the 1830s a great change was taking place in England and in Europe, the start of the steam age and the railway years. The line through Swindon to Bath and Bristol meant the end of the stage coach and so of the Castle Inn. Marlborough was no longer a staging post for traffic to and from the West and in 1843 the old Castle Inn became a public school, Marlborough College, which was founded to be of particular benefit to the sons of clergy. David applied for the post of Medical Officer to the school. His printed application dated 9 March 1843 contained numerous testimonials from medical men – indeed two of them were Fellows of the Royal Society. However, despite this, he was passed over in favour of John Gardiner, who was medical attendant to the Marquess of Ailesbury, an influential member of the newly formed school council. This was the Mr John Gardiner 'who had purchased the business of Mr Washbourne and so gained Lord Ailesbury as a patient and a corporationship for himself'. A much older man than David, having gained his M.R.C.S. in 1812. he had then joined the army and became assistant surgeon to the 1st Foot Guards in 1813 and was at the battle of Waterloo. It is not known when he took over the practice of Mr Washbourne; but it was in 1826 that he had become a burgess of the Borough being Mayor in 1830 and 1834. Surprisingly Mr Washbourne had also remained a member of the Marlborough Town Council and still was in 1835; but it was quite possible to be a member without living in the Borough. John Gardiner retired from the post of non-resident Medical Officer at Marlborough College at the end of 1848 although he remained as a consultant until 1857; from 1849 the College had a resident medical officer, a practice that continued until 1971. Probably soon after 1857 John Gardiner moved away to Cheltenham, but it may have been before then that David became medical adviser to the Marquess of Ailesbury – a practice that was to continue through the generations.

In 1884 *the Memoirs of Life and Work* of Charles J.B. Williams was published by Smith Elder & Co. Professor Williams (1805–89), a physician and professor of medicine at University College, London having been elected at the age of thirty-four, was interested in chest diseases and was also on the staff of the Brompton Hospital. Chapter XXXV of the book is headed 'Country Journeys and Country Practitioners'. He enlarges on the long distances he had to travel before the age of the motor car. A paragraph from this chapter reads:

Many visits did I make in North Wilts – meeting my friend Maurice of Marlborough, who has the best practice in that neighbourhood. Several times I had to see the Marquis and Marchioness of Ailesbury at Savernake, in Marlborough Forest, and once their nephew, the present Admiral Earl Clanwilliam. These visits were very satisfactory and gave me good repute in that Country. I ascribe much of their success to the careful and judicious manner in which Maurice entered into my views and carried them out in practice. His brother at Reading was another skilfull practitioner, with whom it was always satisfactory to hold consultation.

David held various public appointments; he was surgeon to the Marlborough gaol and occasionally received small sums for medical attendance on the prisoners, who for the most part were just vagrants passing through (in 1863 the gaol was finally closed). He was also medical officer to the local Union, which was responsible for the care of paupers. Those registered as paupers and able-bodied were accommodated in the workhouse, together with any wives and children, and made to work. Those not registered as paupers were supported only if they were totally disabled through illness or old age. The Union was administered by a Board of Guardians appointed by the rate payers. England and Wales were divided into 21 districts which had an assistant commissioner who supervised the various Boards of Guardians in their area. The draft Minutes of the Board of Guardians are in the Wiltshire Record Office and throw some light not only on what was involved but also on the unharmonious relations between David Maurice and the rival practitioners in the Borough. Perhaps it was David's success in acquiring the local gentry and aristocracy as his patients that led to this ill feeling.

Originally David's work for the Union covered a wide area to the west and north of the town where so many of his wealthy patients lived, but at some date a Mr Fitzgerald was appointed to look after the parishes for this area and David, who had only one assistant and a flourishing practice, confined his attention more locally. David would probably have received only about £60 for the care of paupers in the Marlborough area but the Union might pay, and pay quite well, for a complicated midwifery case or dealing with severe accidental injuries such as repairing broken limbs. They also paid for vaccinations against smallpox, and they settled bills quickly unlike so many private patients.

Mr Fitzgerald is known to have received £65 annually for the care of paupers in the Kennet valley and then through Avebury to Broad

Town; a very considerable area. However, there were numerous complaints about his lack of care; the Board of Guardians tried to sack him but no one could be found to replace him. His jealousy of David culminated in a flaming row as the records of the Board of Guardians show. One, Charles Major, was taken to the workhouse by Mr Fitzgerald following a severe accident in June 1855. Mr Maurice attended the Guardian's meeting and entered a strong protest against Mr Fitzgerald, who had apparently performed some sort of surgery on Charles Major. Mr Maurice submitted his notes on the case stating that he had seen him at 12.30 a.m. on Monday. He had found him in an alarming state and declined responsibility. On Monday afternoon he had amputated the arm near the shoulder under chloroform. He was doing well at 5 o'clock, and the next day he was doing as well as could be expected but there was much to fear from 'constitutional irritation' which was even worse by Wednesday although as regards the operation all was well. It is not known whether the unfortunate Charles Major survived. Following this Mr Fitzgerald was relieved of his post and David was asked to take temporary charge of the district. At the next meeting of the Board of Guardians they replied to a query from the Poor Law Board in London – 'there is no reason to believe that any other Medical Gentleman in that Union will take charge of that Union on the same terms, not without a very serious increase of expenses which the Guardians in general would not be disposed to incur, and they desire to mention to the Poor Law Board that the Sick Poor of that District have never been attended with greater satisfaction to the Guardians, and it is believed to the Poor themselves, than when the whole Union was, as formerly, under the care of Mr Maurice.' Mr Maurice informed the Board that he intended to appoint a second assistant. Mr Fitzgerald continued to harass David and write letters of complaint to the Poor Law Board. In December 1856 he wrote a threatening letter to David asking him to meet him at the Workhouse. This was passed to the Board of Guardians which sent its clerk, probably a solicitor, to meet him at the appointed time instead of David; Mr Fitzgerald denied it was a threatening letter, but when the clerk produced it he grunted, wished him 'Good morning' and walked off.

Mr Howard Keen was another medical practitioner of Marlborough who repeatedly levelled complaints of neglect against Mr Maurice. Eventually in 1858 it is recorded that 'The Guardians cannot enter upon discussion arising out of imputations on the Medical Officer without again expressing their regret at the ill-feeling notoriously existing among the Medical practitioners in Marlborough, which has on many occasions given rise to investigation and consumption of the time of the Board about personal and professional squabbles without any useful and beneficial purposes'. The mid-19th century was an age of considerable overcrowding in the medical profession and many practitioners had great difficulty in supporting themselves, particularly in rural districts, and so it is hardly surprising if the highly successful David inspired considerable jealousy.

In 1860 David first became a member of the Marlborough Corporation. In 1863 he was Mayor, the first of four generations to achieve that honour. It was an auspicious year as it coincided with the restoration of St Peter's Church and the marriage of the Prince of Wales to Princess Alexandra of Denmark. David performed other public duties: he was a county magistrate and for many years a trustee of the Grammar School. He was Mayor again in 1871 and 1876. In 1854 work started on restoring St George's Church at Preshute. No doubt encouraged by his second wife, he paid for the large stained glass window which dominates the east end of the church over the altar and bears the inscription 'Dedicated to the Glory of God by D.P. Maurice Esq on the restoration of this chancel 1856'.

David's first two children were both girls; his eldest son, named Thelwall after his grandfather, was born on 2 July 1834. He was sent to the Grammar School at an early age when the headmaster was the Revd Thomas Meyler (an old boy of the school himself), sadly he died when only twelve or thirteen; later generations of Maurices were told that rough treatment at the school was the cause of his death. It is true that Thomas Meyler was a strict disciplinarian and the boys were sometimes said to arrive home black and blue as a result of his heavy use of the cane. On the other hand, there may have been some confusion between him and the unfortunate Courtney Boyle Brice, who was so savagely assaulted by Mr Lawes. The fourth child was another girl, and then on 12 December 1837 Marianne gave birth to another son. He was named Oliver Calley and was sent to Marlborough College when only nine years and eight months old. He had over seven years at the College and then decided to train as a doctor and like his father was sent to St Thomas's Hospital qualifying with the M.R.C.S., L.S.A. in 1860 when rising twenty-three. His father was not yet ready for a successor in the practice and so he joined his uncle at Reading. He had a distimguished career there and on two occasions was President of the Reading Pathological Society whch had been founded in 1841. His first Presidency was from 1890 to 1897. In 1901 the Society merged with the Reading Medico-chirurgical Society and he was again President from 1903 to 1904. His son had also become a doctor and had joined his father in Reading, he was President from 1906 to 1908. However, the Maurices managed only three generations in Reading and only two were in direct descent. It was David's third son and youngest child, James Blake, who was destined to succeed him in the practice.

Advances in medical and surgical treatment during the first two generations of Maurices in Marlborough were small. The medicaments doled out by David could have been of no more benefit than those given by his father. Opium for the relief of pain was probably the most valuable ingredient: no doubt this was the principal drug in the 'haust anodyne' so often prescribed by Thelwall and David, particularly in cases of childbirth or broken limbs. However there were two advances which have proved to be the forerunner of much in modern medicine and surgery. The first was vaccination against smallpox – the first step in preventative medicine and the most successful to date, since that often fatal disease has now been totally eradicated throughout the world. The story of how this happened is well known but bears repeating. Edward Jenner (1749–1823) had been apprenticed as a very young man to Daniel Ludlow, a surgeon apothecary in practice at Sodbury, near Bristol. A young country woman attended his surgery one day, she heard something about smallpox being mentioned and at once said she could not catch it because she had had cowpox, a common disease among dairy maids in that area. Jenner moved to London in 1770 to continue his medical education and then returned to his native village of Berkeley, in Gloucestershire, in 1773 to practice as a medical man. Cowpox was uncommon around Berkeley but he used to enquire of his medical brethren what they thought of any possible connection, and Berkeley is not all that far from Marlborough. It was not until 14 May 1796 that he was able to inoculate an eight year-old boy, James Phipps, with matter from vesicles on the hand of Sarah Nelmes who was suffering from cowpox. On the first of July following the boy was inoculated with matter from a patient suffering from smallpox; but he did not catch the disease. An entry in the Day Book on 17 November 1794 reads that 'Thos Kingstone's son was seen at Little Bedwyn' and 'S:pox' is recorded. It was unusual to give a diagnosis but it clearly does refer to smallpox. 'Sm pox' is recorded against another patient;

from subsequent entries it would appear that there was quite an outbreak in the Bedwyn area at that time. Thomas Kingstone's child is recorded as receiving 'ingred. pect' and 'mist anodyne' – and beneath the entry is written inoculating his wife – inoculating his child. The entries are in Dr Pinckney's hand, and just possibly he had heard something from Edward Jenner, although some sort of inoculation against smallpox, but not with cowpox, had been practised for many years. The word 'inoculation' occasionally appears against the name of a patient in the 1800 Day Book, this presumably meant the arm to arm contact with cowpox which was the original method described by Jenner in his pamphlet published in 1798.

The Day Book for 1845 shows that vaccination against smallpox was in full use. Numerous children would be brought to their local school on one day for this to be performed. For example on 30 May 1845, thirty-six vaccinations are recorded on children aged six months to seven years. A single number is entered against this entry, no doubt they were billed to the local authority and the number refers to the page in the other book with the priced items. Where a private vaccination is carried out on a single infant an entry of 4s is recorded against the name when it was paid at the time. Vaccination became compulsory for children only in 1853.

The second advance was the introduction of anaesthesia in the form of ether and chloroform. The benefit of ether inhalation to induce unconsciousness before treatment first reached this country in December 1846. Initially it was used only for dental extraction, but the following year Sir James Simpson was using it in midwifery practice. It soon came into general use. The following is an extract from the *Marlborough Times* of 7 November 1863:

An accident occured at Chisbury on Monday to a steady man named Henry Chandler, in the employ of Mr Cundell, whilst feeding a threshing machine. The poor fellow's day's work was nearly done when he slipped and fell into the drum of the machine, crushing his leg to a pummy, and at once stopping the machine. He was of course removed as quickly as possible and under Mr Lauderdale, of Bedwyn, and D.P. Maurice Esq. and Dr Jas. Maurice of Marlborough, the leg was amputated at the thigh. The operation was skilfully performed under the influence of chloroform, most successfully administered by Dr James Maurice who we understand had considerable experience in such cases while at Paddington Hospital. In a quarter of an hour from inhaling the chloroform the poor man found himself in bed, having no knowledge of the operation. We learn he is progressing as favourably as circumstances will permit.

There is no record of where the operation took place, very possibly in the patient's own cottage as there was no hospital within easy reach of Marlborough at that time. Indeed, amputations of limbs following severe injury could take place at the road side following an accident.

The steam age had led to portable threshing machines with high speed drums which could be conveyed to different farms. Feeding the corn into these machines carried considerable risk of injury and accidents were all too frequent. The Revd J.O. Stevens, the Vicar of Christchurch, Savernake, near Marlborough, had his attention drawn to a farm labourer who had been severely injured in one of these machines. He had to be carried several miles to the house of some medical practitioner, and as only temporary relief could be given he then had to be conveyed to a hospital many miles away. Mr Stephens approached the Marquess of Ailesbury, who at a public meeting on 17 January 1866 offered the Old Training Institution at the top of the hill on the road to London, and bordering Savernake Forest, for hospital services. The building was converted and furnished at the cost of £473 and was formally opened on 30 June 1866. It was the third cottage hospital in England, the first being opened at Cranleigh in 1859. Initially six beds were available but these were later increased to nine. In all 40 patients were treated in the first six months and there were no deaths. The facilities soon proved inadequate, more beds were needed, and further land was donated by Lord Ailesbury. A new building was designed by Sir Gilbert Scott R.A. and built at a cost of £4,960 18s 10d with money raised by subscriptions and charity raising events and was opened on 22 May 1872 by the Bishop of Salisbury. David was appointed surgeon together with Mr R.E. Price – Dr James Blake Maurice and Mr Horace Cooper were appointed Medical Officers. David retired from the partnership the following year and in fact probably did not carry out a great deal of work at the hospital.

David had decided that his son should have Lloran House and so he purchased an extensive piece of land at Manton, one mile to the west of Marlborough. The house standing on it was greatly enlarged with an entirely new brick face and he named it Manton Grange. The Grange stands in its own park and included a farm and a large area of land to the south of the river Kennet. It was to remain family property for the best part of a century. Possibly Rebecca, his wife, may have inherited some of the property from her first husband, but some of it may well have been purchased from the Marquess of Ailesbury, who owned most of the land in the neighbourhood. In addition he acquired Barrow Farm at Clatford, to the west of Manton; no doubt he was preparing for his retirement and for leading the life of a country gentleman. David retired from the partnership on 7 June 1873 and so could continue to manage his estate and fulfill his various public duties. Sadly, his second wife had died in 1867, it would appear to have been a very happy marriage.

David had a farm yard which adjoined Preshute House, one of the Marlborough College boarding houses. This was causing some concern to the Master of Marlborough, the Revd William Farrar, D.D., F.R.S. as the following letter shows. Dated 7 December 1875 and marked private and confidential, it is a good example of Victorian letter writing:

My dear Mr Maurice,

I know that I may safely rely upon the friendliness of your feelings to the College and on the kindness & courtesy with which you have always treated both myself & previous Masters, to give at least your favourable consideration to the matter which I now take the liberty of bringing under your notice.

1. The recent outbreak of fever at Uppingham & its utterly disastrous effects in endangering the prosperity of a flourishing school have called my attention to sanitary matters at Marlborough. Happily the school has been (on the whole) extremely healthy for five years, and you are doubtless aware that the *Lancet* Commissioner in his report on the school puts Marlborough first of them all for sanitary arrangements. In spite of this the undeserved ill name which the school got during the scarlatina outbreaks would cause the most extreme danger not only to the prosperity, but even to the very stability of the College, if anything of the kind were to occur again. It is therefore a subject which needs my most urgent attention.

2. Now in going my rounds it strikes me that the one decidedly weak point in our arrangements is the close proximity of Preshute House to the farmyard in which there is frequently rotting manure, & in which at least one pig is kept. *Most* of the dormitory windows look out immediately on the yard, the smell is not only perceptible, but very strong and indeed a decided nuisance: and the matter is one likely to affect most injuriously the interests of the house & the health of the boys.

3. Now I may tell you (in confidence) that I am forced to the conclusion that, for some reason or other, the health of the boys in that house is (as is abundantly proved by the daily returns of the boys on the sick list) most decidedly below the average of health in every other house. Attacks of illness there are, I can only say it to you privately, more frequent, more serious, & more continuous by far, than they are in any other section of the College. This, I am sure, you will readily accept as a fact to be accounted for and of which the proofs are at hand. I do not say that the immediate proximity of the manure is the *cause* of this, but I venture to ask your opinion as that of a medical practitioner of wide reputation and acknowledged skill, whether it may not have something to do with it? and further whether – even if this be not so – in the unhappy event of any other death taking place in that house, or any serious outbreak of illness occurring

there, both parents and public would not connect the two things together & very seriously blame us if we neglected any means for removing what must be at least a *possible* cause of danger & low stamina? I even take the liberty of going further still, and asking whether, in so unhappy a contingency, you would like the present conditions of things to continue & to be connected with a name so well known in the County as yours? If I am right in assuming that you would on every ground, both of kindness and of desire to befriend the College, regret such results, I cannot but think that you will be ready to meet us half way in any endeavour to remove what may so easily become a cause of public complaint and blame to me and to the College, & which might indeed force us (if there is no remedy) to close the house entirely.

4. Now the immediate object of my writing – at a very busy time – is to ask whether any arrangement can be arrived at either, 1st entirely to remove, or 2nd largely to modify the tenure of the yard? I should be heartily glad & indeed be relieved of what I may call a source of permanent anxiety if you can suggest, or advise any course which may obviate the only too probable consequences which I have indicated.

I have written with the entire trust in the kindness which you have always expressed towards myself, & which I greatly value, I am, dear Mr Maurice

Very truly yours

Frederic W. Farrar

D.P. Maurice Esq.

There is no record of how David responded, but as he remained on good terms with the College it is assumed that he did take the appropriate action.

David's last mayoral year was in 1876. The Tories were in power and Mr Gladstone was between his first and second terms as Prime Minister. He had arranged to stay for a day or two with the Marquess of Ailesbury on his way back from a visit to the Marquess of Bath at Longleat, and had agreed to visit Marlborough College. David wrote to Lord Ailesbury inviting him to bring Gladstone to lunch at Manton Grange. The invitation was accepted and Gladstone duly arrived for lunch accompanied by Lord Ailesbury and his brother, Lord Charles Bruce. According to the *Marlborough Times*, 'on arriving at Manton Grange they partook of luncheon with Mr Maurice, Mr O.C. Maurice of Reading, Dr J.B. Maurice, the Revd. G.C. Bell (Master of Marlborough College – he had succeeded Farrar), the Revd J.S. Thomas (Bursar) and the Rev. G.C. Soames (Rector of Mildenhall). They had travelled thither "in Lord Ailesbury's private omnibus" without attracting much attention. After lunch the members of the Town Council were assembled at the Grange and having been

Group of the four youngest children of David and Marianne Maurice painted by Wainwright in 1843.

Again, the description is taken from the slip found on the back of the picture.

In this group Julia, seated, married James Furnival. Emily, standing behind her, married Thomas Codrington. James Blake, standing on the left and my grandfather, married Agnes, daughter of Nathaniel Kindersley by his second wife, Mary Molesworth and practised in Marlborough. Oliver Calley, seated on the floor also became a doctor and practised in Reading. The picture was painted in the drawing room at Lloran House. Nicholas has the table on the right of the picture.

hospitably received were ushered into the drawing room. When all was ready Mr Maurice entered the room first with his hands behind him in a characteristic attitude – "Gentlemen", he said, "I am walking before the greatest man in Europe." Then came Mr Gladstone with his usual benevolent smile, his necktie slightly awry in the customary way and that charm of manner which conciliated the most bitter opponents'.

A book showing just the charges, not the prescriptions, in 1877 shows that David did very occasionally visit his old patients. One such was a Christopher Day Esq. living in the Pewsey Road. He was visited almost on a daily basis from 1 January until his death on 14 May. He was seen five times on 13 May and two of the visits were made by David who is recorded as seeing him again on 14 May, the day of his death.

David himself died on 16 March 1880 at the age of seventy-eight.

James Blake (1839–1912)

CHAPTER 3

James and the Third Generation

James Blake Maurice was born on 22 October 1839, two years after the birth of Oliver, his only surviving elder brother. He was not sent to Marlborough College but to Cheltenham and then to St Mary's Hospital to study medicine. The Great Western Railway and the foundation of St Mary's close to Paddington Station made travelling to and from that hospital much easier than to and from St Thomas's, and the Maurices have continued to study medicine at St Mary's ever since. He qualified M.R.C.S. in 1861 and L.S.A. in 1862, obtaining an M.D. degree the same year. He travelled in Germany and visited many hospitals and clinics there and held resident posts at St Mary's. In 1864 he obtained his F.R.C.S. and was offered a surgical post at St Mary's. He turned down the option of a Harley Street address in favour of joining his father in practice in Marlborough, initially as an assistant in the practice.

James was a friend of Walter Baskerville, whose father, Thomas, had owned Poulton House. It was Thomas's wife who had owned what was now Lloran House which had been leased to David Maurice at a nominal rent. The Baskervilles still owned the land adjoining Lloran House as far as Figgins Lane and running down to the river Kennet. There was a bridge across the river and they also owned the water meadows on the other side. The Baskervilles had moved to Clyro Court in Herefordshire, where Thomas was the local member of parliament. He died in September 1864 and Walter inherited the Marlborough property; Walter decided it was time James got married and he was invited to Clyro Court for a couple of weeks at the same time as he had another guest, Mary Agnes Kindersley. The match making was a success and by the end of their stay James and Agnes, the name by which she was always known, were engaged. They were married on the first day of February 1866, James was 26 and Agnes 22. On the same day, as a large 8 page document containg 23 clauses shows, James was taken into full partnership with his father. They probably began their married life in property owned jointly by Thelwall's surviving children, but on completion of Manton Grange not long after their marriage they were able to move to Lloran House. Agnes lost no time in starting a family and gave birth to eight sons, followed by three daughters and then

View of the High Street, Marlborough before World War One.

Lloran House. The original building and the Victorian wing added by James. Beyond the tree is, first, the surgery, and second, the house James built for his assistant in the practice.

two more sons. Three of these sons, two of them doctors, Thelwall and Godfrey, were to merit each an entry in *Who's Who*.

When David retired from the partnership in June 1873 James was faced with having to have another assistant in the practice. It may have been this which prompted him to purchase two cottages in Figgins Lane adjoining the surgery and owned by Walter Baskerville. A memorandum dissolving the partnership states that David was to receive £600 annually paid in two instalments half yearly until the day of his death. James now obtained a 21-year lease on the whole of the Baskerville property at the yearly rent of £36 15s paid in four quarterly instalments.

When David died in 1880 James no longer had to pay his annuity of £600. He also inherited half of David's property and possessions less settlements made on his three daughters and so was able to purchase the whole leased to him by Walter Baskerville for £1,000. The articles of agreement of the sale were carried through on 25 March 1881. The Manton Grange property was retained by James but leased out and Clatford Farm was kept to feed his growing family. James now had sufficient money to build an extension to Lloran House, which is the Victorian wing attached to the old Bank House. In addition he built a surgery in the same style where there had been stables and another house beyond this which could accommodate any assistants in the practice. (In 1877 this was Dr Parr, and there was also a full time dispenser.) He enlarged the bridge over the entrance to the stable yard and the entire property could be traversed without going outside. The new surgery was to continue in use as the surgery until 1990, although it was greatly enlarged in the 1950s.

The only Day Book surviving from James's time in the practice is that from 21 October 1890 to 10 October 1891. However there are three ledgers dated 1877, 1897 and 1900. An alphabetical list at the start of these ledgers gives the names of the patients and the page or pages where the name of the patient and the items of service are recorded. These might be a consultation, a visit, or a journey and a visit and the medicaments prescribed. The cost is put against each item and listed at the bottom of the page. The books are large and as many as thirty items are recorded on a single page.

The actual charges for medicaments appear to be much the same as in James's grandfather's time but since patients living in the town or attending the surgery for a consultation had to pay they were doled out in much larger quantities, this might be 7s 6d for an 8-ounce bottle. Some of these medicines were still in use 50 years later, such as bromides for sedation. Others are still in use today, iron for the treatment of anaemia and digitalis for irregular heart beats. However the majority of the prescriptions would still be little more than placebos. James planted a magnificent rose hedge, *rosa mundi*, still known as the apothecary's rose, against the wall on the west side of the garden stretching down to the river. His children were made to pick the buds which were placed in boiling water which added colouring and taste to the medicines. Attendance was added to the charge for the iter made and this depended on the distance travelled and thus the time taken; no distinction was made over the status of the patient. Thus Lord Ailesbury, living 4 miles to the south of Marlborough, was charged the same amount for *iter et attendans* as would a villager living in Ogbourne St George, 4 miles to the north of the town, 5s in each case. Quite frequently a member of Lord Ailesbury's staff required a visit; the cost would be added to the Marquess's account but again whether it was a servant or the Marquess himself the charge would be the same.

A consultation for patients living locally incurred the same charge whether seen in the surgery or in their home, this was usually 2s 6d but might be more if it entailed an evening or a night visit. These books also show that James was called in from time to time by other practitioners living in the neighbourhood. He would appear to have built up a good relationship with the local doctors no doubt aided by his work at Savernake Hospital.

Surgical procedures are only very occasionally recorded on private patients in the 1877 Ledger, usually just dressings or the lancing of abscesses or other minor procedures. No doubt many were carried out at Savernake Hospital and were entered in a separate book there. On the other hand obstetric deliveries are quite frequently recorded, the increasing use of anaesthesia would require the presence of both doctor and midwife. In addition to the deliveries of mothers recorded in the index, three other pages are listed in the index as midwifery cases and record some 80 deliveries. These are charged as a general rule 10s for the doctor's attendance and he was paid at the time of delivery or very shortly after. The assumption is that mothers received some support from the Union but had to pay when the doctor attended the delivery. The private patients were charged one guinea for a normal delivery but for an obstructed labour, retained placenta or some other complication this could rise to three guineas. One private patient who ran up a large bill for her confinement was a Mrs Harrison, who lived in the High Street. She was seen nine

Savernake Hospital, *c.* 1872

times between 7 February and 27 February when James was summoned early in the morning (*primo mane*) as she was in labour. Following delivery she had 'very severe flooding & very long attendance till mid-day'. This is priced at 3 guineas and a further 2*s* 6*d* charged for another visit that day. She was seen six times during the next two weeks and then had a daily visit from March 14 to March 24, when an abscess was incised and she was seen twice. She had a further six visits until the end of the month. The whole confinement cost her about £12, a very considerable sum in those days. The final bill which included a few other items such as vaccinating the baby and extracting a tooth on her son was settled on 20 August, much quicker payment than usual.

The 1877 ledger shows that the practice was still covering the same enormously wide area as in former years. Indeed, some patients lived exceptionally far away and required frequent visits or medicaments for their family or for their employees as well as themselves. One such is Mr Waldron, not even designated 'Esq.', who lived at Upper Lambourne, which must have meant a time consuming journey of some 20 miles there and back on horse back. He was charged £3 3*s* for a visit, £5 5*s* for one in the evening. He ran up a bill for £86 5*s* during 1877 and a further sum in January 1888 because £95 8*s* 6*d* was entered in red (the sign that it had been settled) by James on 1 February. Even Lord Ailesbury was faced with a bill of only £36 18*s* 6*d* for very many more visits and medicines for his family and his staff. On occasion part payments are recorded as being made with sacks of oats or barley, or in one case with a sack of potatoes.

If a patient was seriously ill and lived some distance from Marlborough it must have been a problem to give the necessary attention. A wealthy patient terminally ill does not appear to have been acceptable at Savernake Hospital. Colonel Dawson lived at Stowell, in the Pewsey Vale, which would have meant a ride of some 14 miles there and back. He was visited 107 times between 1 January 1897 and 19 May, the day of his death. Many visits were recorded as being very long and he had to have frequent injections of morphine at the end; no doubt he was suffering from cancer. The total bill was £193 12*s*, well over £8,000 at current values, and was settled on 3 October. At the other end of the scale Mr Duck at St Peter's – Duck's tuck shop close to St Peter's Church was well known to many generations of Marlburians – incurred a bill for 6*s* for a consultation, dusting powder and two 12-ounce bottles of medicine. This bill was never paid: 'Gone to Boer War.'

Patients could be difficult at times just as they are today. One story passed through the generations relates how James was called out one winter's night after a heavy snow storm. A groom arrived on horseback and stated that his master wanted him urgently. James had to get his horse and ride several miles over the downs through thick snow. He arrived shortly after day break to find the master of the house brushing snow away from the front door. James ran up to him exclaiming 'I thought it was you that was ill.' 'Oh no, I only wanted to make sure you could get here if I did need you.'

On 13 December 1848 Dr Walter Fergus had been appointed Medical Officer to Marlborough College. Nothing is known of his relationship with David, but it was probably good, certainly James held him in the highest regard. The 1877 ledger shows that Dr Fergus called James in consultation to see one of the College servants on 1 March and on 29 and 30 July called him in consultation to see 'Sankey Esq.' who was one of the masters. He was also in constant attendance over the Christmas holidays on a servant in the sick house when Dr Fergus would have been away. Dr Fergus retired in 1886 and died the following year. James wrote a long and very fine obituary of him in the *Lancet,* a publication to which Dr Fergus was a not infrequent contributor, and this was republished in the *Marlburian.* To judge by what James wrote 'the good doctor, as he was familiarly called', was extremely popular both in the town and in the College. Dr Fergus was succeeded by Dr Edward Penny, who developed a very close relationship with the Maurices and remained the school medical officer until 1919. He died in 1926.

The ledgers for 1890 and 1897 together with the Day Book for 1890–1891 show how much Dr Penny relied on James and how frequently he called him in for consultation. In those pre-antibiotic days when there was no treatment for such common illnesses as pneumonia or other infections it was not uncommon for a boy to die in the sanatorium. The Day Book for 1890 records that James was called in twice on 9 November, the second time in the evening, to see a boy named Augustin Streatfeild. On 10 November he was called twice more in consultation with Dr Penny. Sadly, the Marlborough College register states that was the day of his death at the age of fifteen. Another frequent reason for James to attend at the College was to perform dental extractions while Dr Penny administered the gas. Altogether James would attend at the College for consultations between 20 and 30 times a month during the school terms, this meant quite an additional income to the practice. One boy, Arthur Purnell, was seen nine times between 1 October and 28 October in consultation with Dr Penny. He survived his illness and joined the army on the the outbreak of war in August 1914 and survived that too.

Not only Dr Penny sought help and advice from James. The ledgers record quite frequent consultations with other doctors in the neighbourhood who sought his experience. The work that he was doing at Savernake Hospital would have given him considerable standing in North Wiltshire. The ledger for 1890 shows that Dr Durdin at Great Bedwyn sought his advice in consultation on numerous occasions and occasionally to perform some surgery on one of his patiemts in the home. He also had to attend Dr Durdin himself when he was ill. The practitioners at Burbage, Pewsey and even Hungerford sometimes sought his advice in consultation.

In 1895 James was appointed medical officer to the Duchess of Somerset Hospital, also known as the Froxfield Almshouses. The

Duchess of Somerset (1631–92) had bequeathed £1,700 to found the Almshouses for poor widows; medical attendance and medicine were provided free. Dr Barker at Hungerford had been the medical officer, but when James applied for the post he was appointed by a narrow majority of the Trustees. His descendants continued to be the official medical officer until the foundation of the National Health Service in 1948 and his great grandson still has patients there today.

It is believed that the only other practice in Marlborough was that of Horace Cooper who was also on the staff of Savernake Hospital, and James was no doubt on good terms with him. The rivalry between members of the profession that had existed in the earlier years of the nineteenth century when it was so overcrowded had largely dissipated. James employed a full time dispenser in his practice and no doubt Horace Cooper also had one and very likely also employed an assistant. In addition to his work in his practice and at Savernake Hospital, Dr Cooper had also been the medical officer of health for six years before his retirement; he was succeeded in all three capacities by Dr T.H. Haydon. After the First World War Dr Haydon joined the Maurice practice in partnership.

Although it could be said that advances in surgery in James's time were greater than those in medicine, it was a French chemist, Louis Pasteur (1822–95) who contributed so much to the foundations of both. The microscope had led to the discovery of bacteria, which at first were thought to be harmless. Pasteur found that they were the cause of infection in animals and so in man. This led to the process of inoculation with attenuated organisms against an increasing number of common diseases. Pasteur himself found that he could prevent rabies in dogs who had already been bitten by a rabid animal by inoculation and with great daring extended the practice to humans with equal success and so saved many lives.

Lister (1827–1912) paved the way for the great advances in surgery during James's time in practice. Anaesthesia had meant that there was no longer the need for just a quick slash with a knife to operate on the limb of a patient, the only open surgery practiced in former times. Abdominal operations were now possible but required time; the advantages of this were largely off set by the appalling suppuration of wounds that ensued. No doubt influenced by Pasteur, Lister decided this was caused by microbes in the air. He first tried to overcome this with the use of carbolic sprays. This was generally adopted by 1875, but the carbolic spray had some disadvantages, the cut surfaces were irritated by the carbolic acid and took a long time to heal. Lister gradually replaced the use of carbolic sprays with the introduction of aseptic methods, the careful washing of hands, the boiling of instruments, the sterilisation of cloths covering the patient and of the surgeon's gown and the wearing of sterilised rubber gloves. He also introduced catgut, prepared from the small intestine of sheep, to replace the silk or flax hitherto used for tying arteries, which, unlike catgut, was not absorbed. Lister's methods were rather slower to be generally used in England than on the Continent but were the common practice by the end of the nineteenth century and the beginning of the twentieth century, although many surgeons were still using weak solutions of carbolic acid when swabbing wounds.

Early records of Savernake Hospital that have survived do not go into any detail but James was a skilful surgeon to judge by what has been written about him and he did keep himself up to date with surgical advances. Until toward the end of the century the majority of operations performed were on limbs, frequently after some serious accident at work and necessitating amputation. As early as 1868 James was operating to remove stones from the bladder and these are labelled and preserved in a glass case. Robert Amber, aged twelve years, had a lithotomy performed on 18 February 1873 – weight of stone 1½ ounces – 'Good recovery'. One early record of an abdominal operation was the removal of an ovarian tumour on Mary Anne Orchard of Baydon. She was admitted to Savernake Hospital on 3 October 1879. 'Friends informed of danger of operation. Discharged cured November 3rd.' Less happy is the case of James Maslen aged twelve. On 23 April 1889 he had pain in the abdomen, castor oil was given – 'good effect'. On 26 April he developed measles – 'no bowel action despite castor oil.' He was admitted to Savernake Hospital on 5 May, the abdomen was opened but he died the same day. Operations for strangulated hernias sometimes appear in these early records John Fishlock aged sixty was admitted on 19 November with a strangulated hernia and had his operation the following day. He was discharged 5 December – 'good recovery'.

Operations for appendicitis only really came into common use in the early part of the twentieth century. It had previously been named perityphlitis, and no doubt had led to many deaths though it would appear to have become much more common in the twentieth century. The practice ledger for 1900 shows that James was frequently called to Marlborough College for consultations, extracting teeth, dealing with fractures and incising abscesses, no cases of appendicitis are recorded. Queen Victoria died in January 1901, and before King Edward VII could be crowned he became seriously ill with an appendix abscess. The successful outcome to his operation led to many more operations being performed and many were carried out in Savernake Hospital during the first decade of the twentieth century.

James was sixty years old at the start of the twentieth century and Godfrey, the youngest of his ten sons, was thirteen on 15 January 1900. All his sons were educated at Marlborough College, although apart from Thelwall, the eldest son, they had boarded at home. James had decided Godfrey should board in the school and he duly took him there at the start of the term, only to find that he had never entered him to go to Marlborough. However, he was duly accepted and boarded at an out college house.

After 1891 James always had at least one of his sons with him in the practice. In 1907 he handed over to two of his sons, Oliver and Walter, who were with him in the practice at the time. He himself continued to assist and received £1,000 annually until 1911 when it had been agreed that the sum should be reduced to £600

James took over care of the Marlborough Union from his father in 1866 and held a number of other public appointments. In 1869 he was appointed surgeon to the Prince of Wales Royal Regiment of Yeomanry Cavalry in the County of Wiltshire, a post he held for many years. He served on the borough council for forty-five years and was an alderman for the last thirty-two, being mayor on four occasions. He also became a county magistrate and became the Chairman of the Bench. He was made a governor of the Grammar School in 1878, when his father was the deputy chairman; in 1880 he succeeded his father in that post. The Marquess of Ailesbury was the hereditary Chairman of Governors. The Grammar School was going through a difficult time after James assumed this office in 1880; it had relied on Boarders, but Marlborough College had begun to accept home boarders and numbers dropped steadily, leading to the school's closure for six years from 1899. After it reopened in 1905 James remained deputy chairman until his retirement in 1909.

James died in Lloran House at the age of seventy-two on 14 February 1912. There is no doubt that he had been held in the very highest repute by the local community and the *Marlborough Times* devoted six columns to his obituary and the account of his funeral. A further tribute was paid to him in a medical magazine published in London on 24 February 1912. Named *THE HOSPITAL The Modern*

Loran House. 1905. Dr James standing beside his carriage, Oliver on the pavement with his children. The wall in front porch. The motor contains members of the family, Walter almost certainly at the wheel.

Newspaper of Administrative Medicine and Institutional Life, it devotes two pages to a long article entitled:

SOME THOUGHTS ON PUBLIC FUNERALS

A Famous Scientific Surgeon and a Great General Practitioner

The first page is devoted to Lord Lister and starts:

> It is well, at a time when politicians, mainly from the absence of sufficient apprehension of the facts and the fulness of knowledge, show a tendency to depart from statesmanship by inflicting needless injustice on members of the medical profession, that public attention should have been directed to, and, as we believe, fixed upon, the true and better side of medicine as typified in the actual life, work, and death of two surgeons widely differing in the fields of labour in which their energies were expended, but united in the testimony which their funerals afford to the inestimable value to the whole community of the daily service rendered by every faithful member of the profession.

The article continues with a long account of the funeral in Westminster Abbey attended by such a large number of his fellow workers, ambassadors of nearly all the foreign countries; representatives of education and science; the Prime Minister and politicians of both parties. Not only the King and the Royal Family were represented but also the German Emperor.

The next page is headed 'A Great General Practitioner':

> Almost contemporary with Lister, and zealously working during the whole of the period in which Lister was fulfilling his destiny by revolutionising surgical treatment, a great general practitioner of the old school, the descendant of a family of surgeons who for generations had rendered inestimable service to the inhabitants of one district of Wiltshire, was in his way revolutionising medical treatment and giving a new hope and prolonged life to hundreds of the poorer people in Marlborough and a wide district around it. On Saturday, February 17, the day after the funeral in Westminster Abbey, Dr James Blake Maurice was buried in Preshute Churchyard, Wilts. Dr Maurice took the fellowship of the Royal College of Surgeons by examination in 1864, some ten years later than Lister. After refusing the offer opened to him to join the staff of a great London hospital, and making a thorough study of German and other foreign clinics, he joined his father in Marlborough and began his career as a general practitioner. A few years earlier, in 1859, Albert Napper had opened the first cottage hospital at Cranleigh; and when Dr James Maurice began work at Marlborough the Savernake Cottage Hospital was soon established. So successful did it prove that a new hospital was opened six years later, and has ever since been proof of the excellent and progressive work these small hospitals can do when they are

blessed with a highly trained and competent medical staff. We went from the funeral to the Savernake Hospital to satisfy ourselves as to the condition of that hospital as it exists today. It is enough to record that out of twenty patients in the beds at least sixteen were surgical cases which had required at the hands of the staff in every instance a major operation. In fact, any surgeon who wished for clinical material for his class could have found nothing better in any hospital in the country. This we take to be a striking confirmation of the confidence placed in him as a surgeon by his patients, the profession, and the public. It further proves the enormous advantage of atmosphere and example, for two out of three of the present staff of the hospital are sons of the late James Maurice, the third being Mr T.H. Haydon, M.B., B.C.

The late James Blake Maurice not only made the Cottage Hospital, with his sons' assistance, so efficient as to enable all major surgical operations to be performed within its walls, but he maintained the great position in the county which his father occupied at the time of his death. The family doctor of half the country-side, fond of his profession, of farming, and of local affairs, several times Mayor of Marlborough, a county magistrate, and the trusted friend of all his neighbours he spent a full and most useful life. From his earliest days he took the greatest pride in his profession, a new course of treatment, a valuable life saved, and an up-to-date operation were to him sources of joy and congratulation. It is recorded of him that he loved his farm, he loved his fellow man, and he never forgot an old friend.

Here then we have presented on succeeding days two great contrasts – the eminent surgeon and scientist on the one hand, and the great general practitioner and surgeon on the other. The memory of the first was commemorated in the most impressive manner in the Abbey of Westminster. The second found his resting-place in a simple country churchyard in the centre of the district where his life work had been accomplished. The work of both men was excellent. The example they set their fellows was great and far-reaching, and the admiration and confidence which each inspired were evidenced in an equally striking and touching manner.

The article continues with a description of the church crowded with all the local dignitaries and the churchyard equally crowded with the many hundreds of people wishing to pay their last respects. It contrasts the simplicity of the funeral in Preshute with the grandeur of that in Westminster Abbey.

CHAPTER 4

The Fourth Generation

The fourth generation of Maurices in the practice overlapped some twenty years with their father. The eldest son, Thelwall, qualified at St Mary's Hospital in 1890 and joined his father as an assistant soon after. James had always had assistants in the practice as well as a dispenser, although little is known about them; it may have been that his one time assistant, Dr Parr, was seeking retirement. After some five years gaining experience in the practice and at Savernake Hospital Thelwall entered the Royal Army Medical Corps. He was to have a distinguished career in the first world war and was awarded the C.M.G. in 1915. In 1919 he was serving in the Afghan War, following which he was awarded the C.B.E. in 1920. This was the year of his retirement. In 1905 he had married Olive, daughter of Sir Henry Burdett K.C.B., K.C.V.O. and they had one son, James (Jim), who was the first of the fifth generation to join the practice.

The second son entered the Church and the third son, Oliver Calley, after training at St Mary's, qualified M.R.C.S., L.R.C.P. in 1893. He was able to join his father before long in place of his elder brother when he joined the army. In 1901 he married Violet, daughter of Henry Giffard of Lockeridge House, and they had two sons. Oliver proved an extremely popular doctor and his old patients were still talking of him in the 1950s. He became a partner of his father and was on the staff of Savernake Hospital. In 1908 Baden Powell founded the Boy Scout movement, Oliver started the Marlborough scouts and their first troop meeting was held on 30 November 1909. He became District Commissioner for North-east Wiltshire.

The fourth son, Ernest Codrington, did have some thoughts on training as a doctor. The records of Savernake Hospital show that he twice was present at operations in 1889 when he had only just reached the age of eighteen. In February he was present in the theatre when his father was amputating an arm, later that year he watched him operating on an irreducible hernia; this was enough to put him off medicine for good and he became an estate agent.

Walter Byron, the fifth son, was born on 5 September 1872. He gained his L.S.A. in 1895 and M.R.C.S., L.R.C.P. the following year. In

The brothers of the fourth generation (the doctors are identified below in italics)

(standing)	Robert	Thomas	*Thelwall*	*Oliver*	Charles	Henry
(seated)			*Godfrey*		Ernest	*Walter*
(cross-legged)					Jack	

1897 he entered the Navy as a surgeon and spent some years in the Mediterranean which he thoroughly enjoyed. Some time after 1900 he was posted to the Royal Naval Hospital at Haslar and it was there that he gained very considerable experience in the art of surgery.

On 31 December 1904 he typed a long letter to his mother. He had clearly spent Christmas at home because the letter begins by saying he had meant while at home to have a talk with her 'about a scheme which has been in my head for some time, and which I expect Father has mentioned to you, namely that I should chuck up the Navy and come to help at Marlborough.' It was clear from the letter that his brother, Oliver – or Tiny as he was always called – was anxious to have Walter in the practice now that their father had reached the age of sixty-five. He enjoyed the Navy and initially it would mean a big drop in income; but it should be possible to extend the practice and were he to postpone his retirement until after May 1905 he would receive a lump sum of £1,000. Walter was now thirty-three, he reckoned the Navy was a poor sort of life if he was to get married since promotion for naval surgeons was a slow business. He was worried lest by postponing his retirement until May he might be sent to sea again in which case retirement would not be possible.

Walter did take the risk and postponed his retirement until after May, when most fortunately for the future of the Maurice practice he joined his father and his elder brother. For the first two years he was to be an assistant and receive £250 annually and boarded free of charge at Lloran House. Thereafter he would join Oliver as a partner and James would receive £1,000 a year for four years and then £600. Oliver lived at Wykeham House, only a few doors down the street from Lloran House; the idea was that eventually he would have Lloran House and Walter would live in Wykeham House.

The exact date on which the practice first acquired a motor vehicle is not known but it was probably about 1904. In the typed document of suggestions for the agreement between James, Oliver and Walter, dated 22 June 1905, one clause states that Oliver and Walter are to provide their own motor vehicles, horses and horse keep after they take over the practice. In 1905 only 75,038 cars were registered in the United Kingdom. The photograph of the family outside Lloran House complete with carriage and motor car shows Oliver with his two children by the porch; this dates it 1907. It was in 1907 that Oliver suffered the devastating loss of his wife, Violet, from tuberculosis. The photograph would have been taken some time after that.

The motor car was not the only invention that began to influence

Oliver Calley (1869–1912)

the lives of doctors in the early part of the twentieth century. Toward the end of the nineteenth century the telephone had been invented but at first there was no national network. Trunk lines began to be allowed only after 1884 and by 1890 telephone services had been extended to 400 towns with about 55,000 subscribers. Marlborough was not one of the towns! One disadvantage of Savernake Hospital is that it is situated a mile outside the town. The first telephone in Marlborough was not connected to any national network but was simply a direct line from Lloran House to the hospital constructed in 1899. It was not until 1919 that the hospital was connected to the Post Office trunk line. Lloran House was number 9; Savernake Hospital, number 59.

The experience that Walter had gained in surgery at Haslar Hospital must have been a considerable asset to the practice. He almost certainly would have taken over much of his father's work as soon as he settled in Marlborough. The ledger for 1910 shows that he twice performed appendicectomies on boys in the sick house at Marlborough College in March of that year. Dr Penny relied very much on the Maurices and they were often called three or four times a week to the College for consultations or some surgical procedure, when Dr Penny would administer the anaesthetic.

On 11 April 1911 Walter married Caroline Edith Tosswill. Her father had been a housemaster at Harrow but was now retired and living at Crowborough in Sussex. Her mother's brother, Henry Richardson, had been a very popular housemaster at Marlborough College; he too had now retired and had acquired some land not far from the Common beside what is called Cross Lane. His retirement home (now named Clements Meadow) was built on this land and Caroline, or Carrie, the name by which she was always known, had for some years been her uncle's housekeeper. She had made so many friends in Marlborough that it was decided that the wedding should take place at Preshute Church with the reception at her uncle's house. The *Marlborough Times* published a very glowing account of the wedding, in which it is alleged, almost certainly falsely, to have stated, 'The church was filled with Dr Maurice's friends and relations and the churchyard was filled with his patients.' Walter was thirty-eight and Carrie was thirty-five. They started their married life in what was then known as Isbury House, the house adjoining the surgery which had been built by James to accommodate assistants in the practice. They lost no time in starting a family and their first child, Timothy Kindersley (always known as Tim) was born on 30

January 1912, some two weeks before the death of his grandfather, James.

Only a few months after James died the practice suffered a terrible tragedy. Oliver contracted pneumonia. Dr Poynton, a specialist from London and a close friend of the family, was hastily summoned. In those days there was no treatment for pneumonia and after only three days, on 11 June 1912, Oliver died at the early age of forty-two. There can be no doubt that not only Walter but the whole town was shattered by his death. His obituary in the *Marlborough Times* begins:

> It is with feelings of the most profound regret, shared as we are sure by every man, woman and child who knew him – and who in Marlborough did not – that we record the death of Dr Oliver Calley Maurice. How familiar seems the name. How much more familiar is the manly, straightforward and genial personality it calls up and how difficult, nay, impossible it is to realise that he is no more. It all happened so suddenly; the one moment he was with us entering with all the vigour of his striking personality into the public affairs of the town, bearing with dignity and humility the mantle which had fallen upon him from his late revered father and the next we are told he has passed from our midst, that Death, the great leveller, whose mighty strength nought can resist, has claimed him and that we shall know him no more.'

In the account of the funeral the paper states

> Grief was plainly written on the faces of all, strong men were shaken with broken sobs, while the women wept freely. Quite early in the morning the flags on public buildings were flying at half mast, while shop fronts bore the ominous black boarding and blinds were down in every house.'

The loss of his elder brother must indeed have been a devastating experience for Walter. He had five younger brothers of whom only the youngest had adopted a medical career. This was Godfrey, who had qualified with his M.R.C.S., L.R.C.P. in 1910. He had held resident posts at St Mary's and at the Hospital for Sick Children at Great Ormond Street. Godfrey was free to come to Marlborough and so he was able to join the practice as an assistant.

Oliver's two orphaned sons were able to remain living at Wykeham House and cared for by their mother's aunt, Miss Hamilton. Agnes, James' widow, moved to a house in Cardigan Road between the High Street and the Common and Walter moved into Lloran House. One duty that Walter did take over from Oliver was that of running the Boy Scouts. He took his place as District Commissioner for North-east

Dr Wheeler   Dr Walter Maurice   Dr Basnall   Dr Haydon   Dr Taylor
Nursing Sister   Matron Lavington   Nursing Sister

Staff at Savernake Hospital between the Wars

Wiltshire and later became County Commissioner for Wiltshire; it would be fair to say that this dominated his life when not involved with his medical career. He was already a member of the town council and became mayor for 1912/13.

Godfrey was not over enamoured with the life of general practice in the early twentieth century. He had probably always hoped that he could pursue a medical career in the army like his oldest brother; Oliver's sudden death had put a stop to this. However, he applied for and was appointed medical officer to the Wiltshire Yeomanry, although he would not at this stage have appreciated the imminence of war. He had had little experience in obstetrics and in later life he said attempting to deliver a baby in a country cottage some miles from Marlborough had been a horrifying experience. Another incident he recounted was when he was called to see an elderly lady at Aldbourne. He found her sitting on a commode beside her bed surrounded by her family. Godfrey exclaimed, 'We must get her back into bed so that I can examine her properly.' 'Doctor, if you do that I shall die.' 'Nonsense,' said Godfrey, 'all heave together.' She was heaved back into bed and promptly died. With some presence of mind Godfrey said, 'I could see she was going to die and if she had died out of bed we should have had to have an inquest.' Not true, but the family seem to have believed him.

Despite the facilities available at Savernake Hospital operations, more especially emergency operations, were sometimes performed in the home during Walter's earlier years in the practice. In 1913 he had to perform an emergency operation in the Pewsey Vale on a patient with a perforated gastric ulcer. He took Dr Penny with him and together with Gunning, the invaluable chauffeur and general handyman, they drove there after dark. The patient was placed on the kitchen table, Dr Penny administered the chloroform and ether and Gunning held an oil headlamp which he had removed from the car to illuminate the proceedings. Unfortunately Gunning fainted but somehow the operation was completed: some 30 years later the patient did get a bed in Savernake Hospital; he was admitted with a fractured femur.

In 1913 Dr Penny had thoughts of retiring from Marlborough College. Godfrey thought that a friend of his, with whom he had shared digs during his student days at St Mary's, would make a suitable replacement and invited him to Marlborough for the week-end. He stayed at Lloran House and accompanied Godfrey on his long rounds which he much enjoyed. He was introduced to Dr Penny and thought him 'a nice man and well up'. However he decided that life would be monotonous. Anyway the outbreak of war in 1914 postponed Dr Penny's retirement. In the fullness of time Godfrey's friend, Charles Wilson, was to become Dean of St Mary's Hospital, President of the Royal College of Physicians and Winston Churchill's doctor. Godfrey was not pleased when he took the title of Lord Moran of Manton. He owned the Mill Cottage at Manton and some time during the 1930s he had allowed Wilson to use it as a country retreat and pay no rent if he did it up and made it habitable. Manton was very much a Maurice preserve; Wilson owned no land or property in the village.

Unlike the second world war the first took the nation entirely by surprise. The Archduke Franz-Ferdinand of Austria-Hungary was asassinated on 28 June 1914; at the time this was not thought to be of any concern to Great Britain. Carrie kept a diary all her life and the first entry relating to any international news was made on July 27 – 'Serbians fired first shots against the Austrians'. July 30 – 'War news worse.' On the following day Walter went with the Marlborough scouts to camp at Barton-on-sea; Carrie accompanied him and stayed in an hotel nearby. Two days later – Sunday 2 August – when the scouts were assembled waiting for a service – Mr Hickson, the scoutmaster, arrived with a newspaper (no wireless in those days) with the news that Germany had declared war on Russia. It was decided that the camp should be broken up and everyone returned to Marlborough. On 4 August 1914 England declared war on Germany – Godfrey received his mobilisation orders the same evening.

Walter at once became involved with the men's detachment of the local branch of the Red Cross Society. An extract from the *Marlborough Times* of 14 August 1914 reads:

Dr W.B. Maurice is acting Commandant in the absence abroad of Mr Herbert Leaf. No time has been lost in perfecting the arrangements for which this Detachment is to be responsible. In addition to regular members of the Detachment, numerous offers of assistance as stretcher bearers, drivers, carpenters, motor cyclists etc. have been accepted.... Several tradesmen in the town have offered the use of their horses and conveyances free of charge for transport purposes. Stretcher practice, conveying "patients" out of trains and placing them on waiting conveyances has already been engaged in.

The same edition of the *Marlborough Times* refers to:

A USEFUL "CLEARING HOUSE"

Our record would be incomplete without a reference to the thoughtful and public spirited action of Dr W.B. Maurice in placing at public disposal the use of a commodious room at Lloran House. This has served as a headquarters for recruiting purposes, for the National Reserve, for the Boy Scouts and for the men's and women's departments of the Red Cross Society, the idea being that the different organisations, all working for the common end, should be kept in touch in one central building while the Scouts have been at the disposal of any or all of them, as well as of the Borough authorities for the delivery of notes and notices and in many other capacities. There being a telephone at disposal and the Post Office being immediately opposite, the use of the building has proved most valuable and it has been greatly appreciated by all concerned.

Godfrey now having been called to military service Walter had to rely on other assistants in the practice. This would not appear to have presented a very great problem; in Carrie's diaries there are frequent references to doctors joining them for meals and at least some of these must have been helping him in the practice. Dr Penny – the College doctor – may well have helped him out too on occasion. As early as 17 August Walter and Carrie were able to take Tim and the nurse to stay with friends at Southwold in Suffolk. They went by train and Walter allowed himself only eight days; Carrie and Tim had a full two weeks.

Surgeons would appear to have been in somewhat short supply in 1914. On 28 October one of the College masters and his wife called at Lloran House; their niece was at school in Monmouth and had developed acute appendicitis. Her parents did not trust the local surgeons: would Walter go to Monmouth and operate on her? He duly left that afteroon and returned the next day. The operation was a success; she was still alive at the age of ninety-four in 1992.

Walter seemed to have regretted that he was not in the Navy now that the nation was at war. An entry in Carrie's diary on 12 November 1914 reads, 'W to the Admiralty wired "no use for me". He found that they had any number of Naval Reserve men & was told it was the same with the army.' He could hardly have considered rejoining the Navy if there were not adequate assistants to run the practice; but it has to be remembered at this time the war was expected to last for only a few months.

Unfortunately, the Day Books relating to the First World War were sent for pulping in the Second World War when paper was so desperately short. However, one incident that Walter was involved in is related by Denis Richards in his biography of Viscount Portal of Hungerford, Chief of the Air Staff in the Second World War.

T.H. Haydon, M.B.
Savernake Hospital 1893–1934

E.R. Wheeler, F.R.C.S.
Savernake Hospital 1929–1952

On the 17 August 1915, young Portal had arrived home on leave from France a day or two before and the family had arranged to have a picnic in Savernake Forest. Portal had gone on ahead and the rest of the family were following in their car. While he was speeding along the road between Hungerford and the forest on his motorbike the front fork broke. He fell forward onto the road hitting his head and hands and bit through his tongue severing the lingual artery. He was lying unconscious on the road and bleeding profusely when the rest of the family arrived in their car and found him apparently bleeding to death. Only a few moments later another car arrived on the scene and halted. As Denis Richards writes, 'The chances of a motor car coming along within a minute or so in 1915 were extremely slender; but the odds against that car containing a doctor must have been beyond computation.' Walter was driving the second car and apparently rushed Portal home and stitched him up – 'so well that in later years the only visible scar was one above his left eyebrow.' It was Admiral Sir Reginald Portal, Lord Portal's younger brother, who told this story; he was to become a patient of Walter's sons after the Second World War.

In addition to all his work at Savernake Hospital and in the practice Walter was also made Medical Officer to the V.A.D. Hospital which was set up in the Wesleyan Hall in Marlborough. Miss Lavington, the daughter of a well-to-do local family, had taken up nursing and she was appointed matron. When the V.A.D. Hospital closed in 1919 Walter persuaded her to become Matron of Savernake Hospital; a post which she fulfilled without pay until 1937. Walter was awarded the M.B.E. in 1919 in recognition of his services to the V.A.D. Hospital.

I was born on 15 December 1915, Walter and Carrie's second son. They wanted to call me 'Dick' because Carrie's uncle, Henry Richardson, had recently died. The boys at Marlborough College had always referred to him as 'old Dick'. One of Walter's younger brothers, Thomas, was a regular naval officer. He had recently lost his life on the *Princess Irene*. This was an ammunition ship and it had blown up off Sheerness killing all on board. They thought that Richard Thomas would be appropriate christian names but Walter kept saying he was sure he knew someone called Richard Thomas but he could not remember who it was. Suddenly he exclaimed, 'Oh of course I know – it is the name of the skeleton in the surgery – he was the last murderer to be hanged in Wiltshire and his body was given to my grandfather for anatomising.' They hastily altered the names to Thomas Richardson, although I have always been called

Dick after my great uncle. In fact, the full names of the murderer were Timothy Richard Thomas!

Carrie's diaries show that Walter carried a very heavy workload. He would often take friends or relations on his rounds, but at least he did now have motor cars, although the roads were largely unmetalled. Godfrey had been commissioned into the R.A.M.C. on a regular basis but on occasion he stood in for Walter when he was on leave. He had a distinguished career in France and was awarded a D.S.O. and a M.C. and was mentioned in despatches. A Dr Clarke Jones is frequently mentioned as helping in the practice and it is surprising how often Walter was able to get away, not only on an occasional holiday but also to see his patients if they were taken ill while away from home. In February 1917 he had to go to Guildford to see one of his patients who had pneumonia. In October he had to visit a patient who had been taken ill in London and then in November his nephew, Jim, Thelwall's son, was taken ill with pneumonia at his preparatory school in Honiton. Walter was summoned there at short notice but was able to return two days later and reported that he was better. In June 1918 he went to Winchester to operate with a Dr Wickham.

With the proximity of Salisbury Plain and air training bases aeroplanes became a common feature over the town during the war. The pilots used to indulge in stunt flying; on occasion they were even said to fly their planes under the telephone wires that crossed the Marlborough High Street from roof-top to roof-top. One day in May 1918 a pilot came running into the town asking for a doctor. He was directed to the surgery and told Walter he had been deliberately frightening two girls in a field near Avebury when the wing of his plane struck one of the girls on the head. He had seen her lying in the field, apparently unconscious, and had flown to Marlborough and landed on the Common. Walter said he would drive over immediately but the pilot said there was no time for that, he must fly him over. Walter drove him to the Common and boarded the plane, his first experience of flying. They landed close to the girl with a terrible bump: she had a fractured skull: Walter managed to get some transport to take her to Savernake Hospital and asked the pilot to fly him back to collect his car. The pilot exclaimed – 'Don't you realise we can't do that? We crashed on landing.' Walter is believed to have travelled back with the girl and happily she recovered.

Acute appendicitis seems to have been much more common in the first half of the twentieth century than it is today. Walter actually performed seven appendicectomies on Marlborough College boys in the summer term of 1918. To judge by the brief entries in Carrie's diaries relating to other doctors, it was none too easy to get locums or assistants in 1918. However, Walter and his family managed to take a two week holiday in Devonshire from 15 July; this was fortunate as the world wide epidemic of influenza spread to England toward the end of the summer. Mr Lalor, the dispenser, was one of the early victims at the beginning of August. By October Walter was desperately overworked – 18 October – 'W. very busy – influenza epidemic.' 28 October – 'W. very overworked.' 29 October – 'Dr Haydon ill – W. seeing nothing but influenza.' However, at least the Germans were now in full retreat and on 10 November the Kaiser abdicated and the armistice was signed the following day. Meanwhile there was no let up in the influenza epidemic, Walter himself had a mild attack but went on working. There was, in fact, little that doctors could do for influenza sufferers and the resultant pneumonia in 1918 – Walter is believed to have lost forty of his patients. Worldwide twenty million persons are said to have died in the space of a few months – far more than lost their lives in the war.

Walter does seem to have had some assistance in the practice in early 1919 from a Dr Phillips, and Godfrey helped out for a time in March when on leave. The minister for war, Walter Long, lived in Wiltshire. Walter knew him and appealed to him to have Godfrey temporarily released from the army. Godfrey was allowed his release and he duly came as an assistant on 21 June 1920 and remained for about a year before going back into the forces. In 1921 he was seconded to the Egyptian army and became principal medical officer to the Sudan Defence Force. He retired in 1931 but rejoined the army in the Second World War and served in North Africa and Italy.

On 1 July 1919 Walter and Dr Haydon entered into full partnership; since that date there has only been one practice in Marlborough but they continued with their separate surgeries and each had his own dispenser. Dr Haydon's surgery was behind his house, now part of the Castle and Ball Hotel, on the north side of the High Street. Only in 1955 was the Maurices' surgery enlarged sufficiently to accommodate the four partners then working in the practice. Dr Penny retired from his appointment of medical officer to Marlborough College at the end of the summer term in July 1919 and Dr Hallows was appointed in his place. Thereafter, Walter did very little work for the College; Dr Hallows was a highly qualified physician and had a good knowledge of pathology such as it was in those days. The practice had possessed a microscope since the end of the nineteenth century but Dr Hallows could report on blood specimens for Walter and he was appointed pathologist to Savernake Hospital. Before the National Health Service was instituted all appointments to the staff of the hospital were honorary.

On 1 December 1920 the practice gained a new partner. Dr E.C. Taylor was only a few years younger than Walter and had pursued his medical career in India. Sadly, his wife had developed pulmonary tuberculosis, from which she was to die only a very few years after coming to Marlborough, and probably this had led to his return to England. They had two young sons, the older one was close to me in age, and a daughter. Dr Taylor worked in Walter's surgery. Walter had his consulting room in Lloran House. Each partner was on call to Savernake Hospital for one week at a time. This rota system was first introduced in 1893 when James's eldest son, Thelwall, joined his father. Dr Haydon was on call for one week in three.

Although all three partners had very considerable surgical experience they did on occasion refer non-acute patients to London between the wars. The big London teaching hospitals accepted patients from all over the country and Walter would sometimes refer his patients to St Mary's when they required such operations as a hysterectomy. In 1925 a very unusual appointment was made for a cottage hospital, a visiting consultant. Mr, later Professor, Girdlestone, was the orthopaedic surgeon at Oxford. He is believed initially to have come to Savernake monthly to undertake an operating list. Through him Savernake developed a close relationship with Oxford; he was the first of many consultants to come from Oxford's hospitals. Walter was fond of telling how once Professor Girdlestone had to operate on a patient's knee. The patient also required an appendicectomy; they decided both operations could be performed simultaneously. Orthopaedic surgeons, quite rightly, are very careful about sterilisation and the prolonged scrubbing of hands before putting on their gloves. They started scrubbing up together and after a time Girdlestone was heard to say 'Are you ready Maurice?' 'Ready! – I am just sewing up.'

One family that relied heavily on Walter between the wars were the Wills's, who had purchased Littlecote. Sir Ernest Wills was Lord Lieutenant of Wiltshire. On two occasions Walter was sent for urgently and had to travel to the continent. Once he had to go to

Switzerland when Lady Wills's nephew had some abdominal trouble, and on another occasion he had to fly to Paris and board the night express to the French Riviera when Lady Wills was suffering from a skin complaint that was thought to be an allergy.

There were only some twenty beds in Savernake Hospital at the end of the First World War and the operating theatre was small; quite major operations were carried out in the home if facilities there were satisfactory. Chloroform and ether dripped onto a face mask was still the method of inducing anaesthesia and this did not present a problem. Further, there was less risk of cross infection from another patient in the hospital. It was always possible to get nurses down from London to care for the patient. The Marchioness of Ailesbury was suffering from gall stones and Walter operated on her at Tottenham House, the Ailesbury residence in Savernake Forest, on 25 January 1922. However, many operations were carried out at Savernake Hospital – indeed, Carrie's diary records that Walter performed seven operations there on 21 February 1922.

On 2 December 1923 two operations were carried out in the day nursery at Lloran House. Walter's nephew, Alec, had been suffering from attacks of abdominal pain for some time and it was decided to remove his appendix. His son, Tim, had an operation for a hernia. A nurse came from London to care for them. I was taken with my nurse to stay with Alec's parents at Manton Grange. Surgery on private patients in the home provided some additional income, although in general charges for medicines and attendance on patients were much the same as in Walter's grandfather's time. The Day Book for 1920 records an operation for acute appendicitis at Wilcot – a good seven miles from Marlborough. This and three attendances in the next five days was billed at £21. Medicines were if anything cheaper than in great grandfather Thelwall's, time. They were given out in much larger quantities and charged between 1s and 2s 6d. Until well after the Second World War the greater part of a general practitioner's time was taken up in visiting patients in their own homes. Only the very well to do gentry would possess a motor car and these for the most part would expect the doctor to visit them rather than go to see him. The majority of those living in the local villages would have no means of getting to the surgery. However, Walter did have a branch surgery in Avebury which he attended twice weekly and this was of some assistance to patients in that area. Visits in Marlborough itself were made far more often than they are today when measles, whooping cough and other infections took up so much of the doctor's time.

In 1911 Lloyd George had implemented the National Insurance Act. Weekly wage earners were compulsorily insured and had sickness and maternity benefit for their wives; a considerable help to the working classes. Visits to patients living locally were costed between 3s 6d and 7s 6d. Where an iter was involved this would rise to somewhere between 10s 6d and one guinea depending on the distance. The 1920 ledger shows that Mr Lalor, the dispenser, costed everything in pencil; a 5s entry might sometimes be increased to 7s 6d in ink. Walter's annual income in the 1920s sometimes reached as much as £2,000. On this he could afford two or even three cars, a cook, parlour maid, house maid and my nurse. He employed a chauffeur and gardener full time, although they lived in cottages owned by him, and pay for Tim's preparatory school fees at Swanage; this cost £50 per term.

The 1920s and '30s were the decades of great development at Savernake Hospital. It was dependent entirely on voluntary financial help but had a wide reputation and gained many benefactors, for which Matron Lavington must take much of the credit. The Ailesbury family had contributed so much from the start, but now they were joined by such well known names as Sir Ernest Wills, Viscount Astor, Lord Nuffield and Lord Rootes to name but a few. Money was also raised by annual subscriptions and collections from all the local churches. Many local events such as fetes, football matches, concerts and Hospital Weeks all helped. The annual Pewsey Carnival was of particular benefit. In 1928 the Hospital Contributary Scheme was started, within eighteen months it had 10,000 members and produced £5,483.

In 1927 the Marchioness of Ailesbury opened a large new ward, first used for men, a children's ward, and isolation rooms, later used for private patients. A primitive Röntgen ray apparatus had been in use since before the war but now X-ray facilities were upgraded over the years and brought fully up to date before the Second World War. A nurses' home was built in 1931 and a magnificent operating suite with anaesthetic room, theatre and recovery room was opened in 1935. Facilities at Savernake were quite as good or better than anything in Swindon and the beds grew to 100. The catchment area remained as always and included not only Marlborough but Ramsbury, Hungerford, Pewsey and much of the Pewsey Vale, Burbage and Bedwyn.

The Marlborough practice continued to be responsible for day-to-day care and dealing with all emergencies but practitioners from local

Walter (1872–1956) in retirement

villages, particularly Dr Bashall from Burbage, gave their services as extra anaesthetists. He started work at Savernake Hospital in 1929 and that was the year the practice gained a new partner. Dr E.R. Wheeler was a Fellow of the Royal College of Surgeons and had been a medical missionary in China. Of much the same age as Walter and Dr Taylor, he joined Dr Haydon in his surgery; this must have afforded some relief to Dr Haydon, who was now able to carry out less work; he retired in 1933.

Although appointments to Savernake Hospital were all honorary, specialists in various fields became attracted to its staff; no doubt they would also get some private work. Dr Monnington was a physician at Salisbury and he became a consultant at Savernake in 1929. During the '30s a Mr Tait, an oculist from Windsor, was appointed and Mr Atkinson, an ear, nose and throat surgeon, from Bath. In 1938 Mr J.C. Scott, an orthopaedic surgeon at Oxford, joined Professor Girdlestone who was about to retire. He gave invaluable service to the hospital and when called into the R.A.F. in the war was stationed for the most part at Wroughton, only a few miles from Marlborough, and was able to continue his services to Savernake. In 1934 Walter's nephew, James Burdett, but always called Jim, joined the practice when Dr Taylor retired. His father was Walter's eldest brother, Thelwall. Jim was friendly with Arthur Porritt, later Lord Porritt, a surgeon at St Mary's, and he was appointed consultant surgeon to Savernake for some two years until he joined the services in the war. There appears to have been a good relationship between the Marlborough practice and other doctors in the surrounding area. The ledger for 1930 contains a two page list of consultations with other practitioners who had called Walter to see their patients.

The greatly increased size of Savernake Hospital after its extension in 1927 meant much more work for the Marlborough doctors, but in 1930 new responsibilities fell on Walter. The County Council took over the management of the Union, or workhouse, from the local parishes. Demand for accommodation there had largely fallen off and it was decided the building should become a convalescent home for Wiltshire children, leaving just a few beds for vagrants passing through. Walter became involved from the start and was appointed the medical officer. Sixty years ago children suffered from many chronic illnesses which required long periods of convalescence. Tuberculous glands in the neck from drinking unpasteurised milk was one frequent cause for admission. Children recovering from poliomyelitis or from osteomyelitis, infection of the bones, also accounted for many admissions. There were babies suffering from rickets and some children with congenital abnormalities. Mrs Harral was appointed matron in 1932 and like Miss Lavington was a tower of strength. Children admitted were essentially convalescent from their illnesses and were not confined to bed. Walter would frequently take three or four on his rounds when visiting his country patients, few of them would ever have had much opportunity to travel in a motor car in those days.

In 1939 Walter's elder son, Tim, joined the practice. Jim had hoped to study for his Scottish F.R.C.S. but war was looming and on 3rd September Neville Chamberlain announced that we were at war with Germany. Jim was in the Royal Air Force Volunteer Reserve and was immediately called up and was destined to serve in the Middle East. The Children's Convalescent Home became a War Emergency Hospital; the children were sent home or to other institutions and initially it was filled with blind evacuees from London, which was expected to be heavily bombed on the outbreak of war. Later it was used for many purposes, but mainly for the accommodation of the elderly sick. Walter was now aged sixty-seven, two years past retirement age for general practitioners today. He was to have seven more years of a very heavy workload with Dr Wheeler and Tim and any locums they could get to assist in the practice.

In April 1947 I joined the practice. My father, Walter, was now seventy-four years of age and had experienced working through two world wars when the practice was desperately short-handed. He finally retired in 1948 at the start of the N.H.S.

There were some notable advances in medicine during Walter's time in practice prior to the Second World War. Sir Frederick Gowland Hopkins had discovered the value of certain substances, which he named vitamins, in foods which could prevent scurvy and rickets. In 1921 Banting and Best introduced insulin for the treatment of diabetes and so saved many lives. In 1926 it was found that raw liver taken by mouth would save the lives of those suffering from that hitherto fatal disease, pernicious anaemia. Sadly this was two years after Walter's sister had died from it. It was only after the war that the active component, vitamin B12, could be given by injection. In 1937 prontosil, the first of the sulphonamides, and the first drug that could cure bacterial infections, became available. Prontosil was soon replaced by better sulphonamides which saved many lives during the war. Although the ledgers for 1920 and 1930 do show some medicaments such as digitalis were of real benefit the medicines prescribed were still for the most part just placebos.

Walter died on 13 September 1956 at the age of eighty-four, his nine brothers and three sisters had all predeceased him.

CHAPTER 5

The Fifth Generation: Part One

SOME PERSONAL MEMORIES
by
Tim Maurice

From my earliest youth I never had any doubt that I would be a doctor. In part this was probably due to brain-washing. I often accompanied my father on his rounds and when he left a patient's house a member of the household would frequently escort him back to his car and when he saw me would remark, 'Of course you will be following in your father's footsteps – won't you?' To be fair, my father never brought any pressure to bear himself. Indeed, on one occasion when I suppose I was about sixteen he told me that one of his wealthy patients who had a big tannery business had suggested that I might consider joining his firm; this would involve some time in South America learning about the job from the grass roots. I can still recall the look of relief on my father's face when I said, 'But I want to be a doctor'.

I went from Cambridge to start my clinical work at St Mary's Hospital in 1934. In those days chemotherapy had not been thought of, let alone the use of antibiotics. I can still remember Mr Leslie-Williams, one of the consultant gynaecologists, informing us that three things were required in the treatment of puerperal sepsis (all too common a problem then) – 'good food, God and Guinness'. Alexander Fleming taught us bacteriology and would demonstrate how if he introduced some *penicillium* mould onto a plate with a culture of *streptococci* or *staphylococci* they would die off and disappear while another organism, *bacillus coli*, would continue to flourish. So few patients were delivered in hospital that there was insufficient material in the small maternity department at St Mary's to give us a proper introduction to midwifery; accordingly we were seconded for a month to Queen Charlotte's Hospital, then situated in

Timothy K. 'Dr Tim'

the Marylebone Road. We were billeted in Cosway Street on the opposite side of Marylebone Road. At night, whenever a patient was about to be delivered, a loud bell would ring and we would all dash across the road in our dressing gowns. Blood transfusion was a major operation. Anyone who was group 'O' was regarded as a suitable donor, this was before awareness of the rhesus factor. The donor lay on a bed adjacent to the patient. Blood was withdrawn from the patient into a three-way syringe, the so called rotunda syringe, it was then passed into a bottle containing citrate to prevent clotting, withdrawn again and then pumped into the patient. The whole process was repeated until one hoped the patient had received about a pint of blood, but a fair proportion always seemed to end up on the floor.

I qualified with the 'conjoint', M.R.C.S., L.R.C.P. in July 1937. A week later I started a 'locum' job at Rye in Sussex. In those days one did not have to do a further year in hospital before getting onto the medical register. I was to stand in for the junior partner and assumed that the senior partner would keep a careful eye on me; unfortunately it transpired that he imbibed so much in the evening that he seldom rose before midday. I went to the opposition firm and put my cards on the table and they nobly helped me with advice whenever I felt I was getting out of my depth.

On 1 October I returned to St Mary's as house physician to Dr Charles Wilson, later to become Churchill's doctor, Lord Moran. At this time prontosil, the first of the sulphonamides, was just coming into production. One day, in the course of a ward round, Dr Wilson said, 'Tell me Tim, what is this stuff protonsil that everyone is talking about?'

My six months as house physician finished at the end of March 1938 and on 20th April I married Philippa Sharp whose father, then deceased, had been a prominent G.P. in Truro. We had been engaged for 2½ years and through three reigns, but to marry while not yet qualified was almost unheard of in those days. In June I sat and successfully achieved my Cambridge M.B. B.Chir degree. During the next two months, accompanied by Philippa, I did two more locum appointments: the first at Colyton, near Seaton in Devon, and the other at Padstow in Cornwall. The single-handed doctor in Colyton took me round his surgery before leaving for his native Glasgow and showed me three large flagons of medicine coloured pink, yellow and brown; he explained that he dispensed them in turn to his chronic patients so that they had a different-coloured brew each time; this seemed to do them more good than always having the same colour. What these placebos contained other than colouring agents I cannot recall. I was called from my bed one night to a remote farmhouse near Honiton where I found the farmer's son aged about twenty suffering from acute appendicitis. When I said we must get the ambulance I was assured that the Honiton ambulance ran only by day which indeed proved to be the case; I had to put the patient in my car and drive him 15 miles to the Royal Devon and Exeter Hospital. His appendix was removed before breakfast on the point of perforation and so the journey was worthwhile.

At last, on 1 July 1939, I returned again to St Mary's as resident obstetric officer; my chiefs were Alec Bourne, Leslie-Williams and Douglas MacCleod. Three more different men it would be hard to imagine but all were excellent teachers and I greatly enjoyed my six months with them and developed an interest in obstetrics which remained with me for the whole of my professional life.

At last, on 1 July 1939, I joined the Marlborough practice as an assistant for one year on a salary of £400, with the understanding that I would then become a partner. My place in the practice had been kept warm for me for the past two years by Dr Donald Wilson; he had accepted an assistantship in the practice when Dr Taylor retired as he wanted to gain experience but knew that I would be taking his place in due course. He had been a contemporary of my cousin, Jim, at St Mary's and went on to become a consultant physician.

Two months later we were at war. Jim was on the R.A.F. Volunteer Reserve and was immediately called up. My father, Walter, was sixty-seven, Dr Wheeler was sixty-two and the town was overflowing with evacuees. Within a few days Dr Tangye, the County M.O.H., arrived and explained that I must under no circumstances volunteer for one of the services; I was more useful where I was and indeed it would be very difficult to provide adequate medical cover for the town without me. So I spent the war in Marlborough, but it was not a sinecure.

At this time the medical staff of Savernake Hospital, apart from the few visiting consultants, were the members of the Marlborough practice and Dr Bashall, the G.P. in Burbage, some six miles from Marlborough, who specialised in anaesthetics. All the operations were carried out by Dr Wheeler or my father with Dr Bashall giving the anaesthetics or myself if he was unavailable. He never came for emergency operations at night, those anaesthetics fell to me. We, the three Marlborough doctors took it in turn to cover casualty. Until 1939 the maximum number of deliveries in a single year at Savernake had been twenty-eight. The difficulty of finding carers for a home delivery in the war resulted in an immediate large increase in the numbers seeking to have their babies in hospital and they came not only from our practice but from all the surrounding area, Pewsey, Ramsbury, Hungerford etc. Dr Wheeler continued to look after his own maternity patients but all the others fell to me and I very soon started an antenatal clinic at Savernake, initially once a week but very soon twice a week. If a Caesarian section was needed Dr Wheeler operated but all the other obstetric complications I dealt with myself. I soon found myself being called from my bed two or three times a week and on one occasion I was actually called out on sixteen consecutive nights. I once went for a whole year without a night out of Marlborough or a night off call. As I have said, it was not a sinecure. The days were hectic too. Most days there were two or three surgery sessions and even on Saturdays I had an evening surgery which ofter lasted from 6 until 8 p.m. In order to earn a reasonable income we had to have well to do private patients many of whom lived as much as ten or twelve miles away; it was not unusual to drive over 50 miles in a day.

Whenever there was a slight lull in the volume of work something always seemed to crop up. We had a small isolation hospital next to what had been the Children's Convalescent Home, now a War Emergency Hospital, on the edge of the Common where we always had a few cases of scarlet fever and in the winter we frequently had cases of diphtheria. Exactly when I do not recall, but in one quiet patch we suddenly found ourselves with an epidemic of cerebro-spinal meningitis. More than thirty cases were admitted to the isolation hospital over about two months. The treatment then was massive doses of sulphonamides which often resulted in horrific rashes but their worth was proved by the fact that we had only two deaths.

During another lull a baby that had just arrived in Swindon from India developed smallpox. The designated smallpox hospital for the area was a hutted building half way between Swindon and Marlborough for which we in Marlborough were responsible. No case of the disease had ever been treated there and at the time it was fully occupied by geriatric evacuees. These had to be sent to the emergency hospital on the Common at a few hours notice and the baby was admitted. Over the next week we vaccinated about 2,000

James B. 'Dr Jim' (1906–1979)

people in the Marlborough area, many of them adults who had never been vaccinated and telephoned a week later complaining of inflamed arms. Several persons developed a generalised vaccinia and had to be admitted to the smallpox hospital for observation until we were sure that they were not smallpox cases. In fact the baby had infected a teenage boy and a man in his forties who had never been vaccinated and very nearly died. The man left hospital eventually terribly scarred and looking a wizened old man. The baby and the boy both made good recoveries.

It was not only epidemics that gave us sudden increases in the work load. As I was leaving the surgery one morning about 11 a.m. a policeman stopped me and said that there had been an accident on the Salisbury road at the foot of the hill leading down from Savernake Forest. I drove straight there and to my horror was confronted by an overturned army truck in a field and twenty-three soldiers lying there and groaning. The brakes of the truck had failed and it had crashed through a fence. Twelve of the injured had to be admitted to Savernake Hospital with fractures and other injuries including a ruptured spleen. A team came over from the Wingfield-Morris Hospital in Oxford to assist with the fractures. I had to administer the anaesthetics and did not get home until breakfast time the following day.

On a September evening in 1943 I was called urgently to the hill leading up to Savernake Hospital. Lying in the middle of the road was the assistant cook at the hospital stone dead with two bullet wounds in her back. It was known that she had been to the cinema with the hospital secretary's typist of whom there was no sign. Three hours later the typist staggered into the hospital having witnessed the shooting by a coloured American soldier who had then marched her off at gun point and raped her. Fortunately he had left his forage cap at the scene of the rape and the troops stationed in the forest nearby to guard the ammunition stored there were quickly paraded; the one without his forage cap was arrested. I was involved in endless reports, a trip in a jeep to Castle Cary in Somerset to determine whether the rape victim was fit to testify and giving evidence myself at the American court martial. Both murder and rape were capital offences and the accused was hanged at Shepton Mallet.

At times during the war we were able to obtain the services of an assistant in the practice but for one reason or another none of these were full time workers and the one who stayed longest was so unreliable as to be almost more trouble than he was worth.

By the time the war ended my father was almost seventy-three and Dr Wheeler was sixty-eight and it was a tremendous relief when Jim was demobilised in early 1946 to be followed a year later by Dick, who gradually took over Walter's patients. In 1952 Dr Wheeler retired and was replaced by his son, Bob, who was also a fully trained surgeon.

We viewed the advent of the National Health Service in 1948 with some trepidation but adjusted to it quickly and, over the long term, found it of enormous advantage to us and to our patients. One of our great reliefs was no longer to have to send bills, albeit very modest ones, to patients who could ill afford to pay them; also we were much less dependent on wealthy private patients for our livelihood. We were now paid on a sessional basis for our work at Savernake Hospital, which previously we had carried out voluntarily so that overall we found ourselves financially much better off.

I was one of the two or three G.P.s who were invited to serve on the Swindon and District Hospital Management Committee from its inception in 1947, and I remained a member until 1971. This gave me a fascinating insight into the medical services of the Swindon area. In July 1948 when the National Health Service came into being there were only three consultants in the town, a general surgeon, a physician and a gynaecologist. The population of Swindon at that time was about 60,000 but its hospital, the Victoria, was approximately the same size as Savernake. In addition, there was a geriatric hospital a mile or two away at Stratton St Margaret and also a small G.W.R. Hospital, which served only employees of the Great Western Railway and their dependants. All anaesthetics were given by the local G.P.s and an E.N.T. surgeon came over from Bath once a week to deal with any problem in that field.

It was apparent that there was a crying need for a large modern hospital but it was impossible to make a start so soon after the war. However a site was chosen, architects briefed, and in 1957 Princess Margaret, after whom the hospital was to be named, duly laid the foundation stone. By 1960 it was in full swing, with a large resident staff and a consultant staff in every branch of medicine. However the actual official opening, again by Princess Margaret, was delayed until 27 April 1966. This was the first post-war District General Hospital to be built in England; if one wanted proof of the need for a National Health Service this was it.

Savernake Hospital came under the umbrella of the Swindon and

District H.M.C. but the Oxford consultants continued to supply the greater part of its consultant service. The general surgeon, orthopaedic surgeon and the obstetrician and gynaecologists attended twice monthly for out patient consultations and operating sessions. The consultant physician also came from Oxford and did a bi-monthly out patient session in the afternoon followed by a ward round. He always had a picnic lunch in Savernake Forest before coming to the hospital. Initially, Bath supplied an E.N.T. consultant and an ophthalmologist came from Windsor while a pathologist came from Salisbury.

During the late 1960s with the completion of the Princess Margaret Hospital and the steady increase in the number of consultants in Swindon more and more of the consultant service was supplied from Swindon although Savernake continued to draw on Oxford for its orthopaedic consultants.

In my own special field of obstetrics and gynaecology we were very fortunate soon after the end of the war to obtain the services of Mr (later Sir) John Stallworthy and his Oxford colleague, Mr Hawksworth, who took it in turn to hold the bi-monthly out-patient and operating sessions. They regularly performed major operations such as hysterectomies. At no time has there ever been a resident doctor at the hospital and we, the G.P. members of the staff, really acted as registrars to the consultants. We had to ensure that the patients were fit for operation, transfusing where necessary prior to operation and having to take full post-operative responsibility, but the system worked very well. For myself it was a great relief no longer to have to take full responsibility for the more complicated obstetric problems and every endeavour was made to ensure that any patient likely to require Caesarian section was transferred to Oxford for delivery. By this time we were delivering about five patients a week at Savernake, including quite a high proportion of forceps and breech deliveries but only about once a year did we have to call on the Oxford Flying Squad because a section had become necessary.

As soon as time permitted after the war, in 1947, I had sat for and obtained my diploma from the R.C.O.G. With the advent of the health service I was given five notional sessions per week at Savernake, each of 3½ hours, four in obstetrics and one in general medicine. In 1949 Dr Bashall retired from his practice in Burbage and became a full time consultant in anaesthetics for the Swindon area. His place was taken by Dr Hassall, who was appointed to help with the antenatal clinics and cover for me for obstetrics when I was off duty or away. Later, as the hospital maternity work steadily increased, Dr Tiplady, a G.P. from Ramsbury, was also appointed to the Savernake staff to help with clinics and obstetric cover. One problem was the absence of a labour ward. Normally we delivered our patients in the anaesthetic room adjacent to the operating theatre, but when operations were in progress we just had to take whatever space was available. Usually there would be a small vacant side ward, but I can recall delivering the wife of a Marlborough College master on the X-ray table, and on another occasion conducting a delivery behind screens in the corridor leading down to the Nurses' Home. It was a great relief to all concerned when a labour ward was built in 1955. By the mid-1960s Princess Margaret Hospital had an excellent maternity unit and we turned to them for our obstetric cover. Sad as it was to sever our links with Oxford it was a great comfort to know that Flying Squad aid was only 12 miles away instead of 40 miles as heretofore.

I regard myself as extremely fortunate to have lived my professional life through the middle decades of the twentieth century, a time of the greatest advances in medicine that the world had ever seen. However the advances continue so that a young doctor qualifying today probably thinks that we were a pretty primitive lot when I retired some sixteen years ago.

CHAPTER 6

The Fifth Generation: Part Two

Tim has written something about his earlier years before joining the practice and so perhaps I may be forgiven for doing the same. Like him no pressure was brought on me to study medicine and indeed I did think of taking up printing as a career. However medicine seemed to have more to offer and I followed Tim to Pembroke College, Cambridge. In 1937 I began my clinical work at St Mary's Hospital. On the outbreak of war in September 1939 I was nine months from beginning to sit the first of my final examinations. The Hospital was evacuated to various sector hospitals to avoid the expected heavy bombing of London. I was sent to Park Prewett Hospital at Basingstoke which we shared with St Thomas's Hospital. However the bombing did not materialise in those early months and we had virtually no patients. After three months with no clinical work we returned to St Mary's. At the end of August and the beginning of September 1940 the bombing of London really got under way. I soon evacuated my rooms and moved into the basement of the laboratory building at the hospital. We were joined there by Alexander Fleming who slept in the first camp bed. Next to him was Mr Handfield Jones, the senior surgeon, and then Dr Hope Gosse, the senior physician. We often worked through the night dealing with casualties, but morale remained high in the hospital and the consultants, junior doctors and students got to know each other in a way that would be unthinkable in peace time. Indeed I am still in regular contact with five of my fellow medical students from those days.

I qualified M.R.C.S., L.R.C.P. at the beginning of January 1941 and then did six months as house physician to Dr Hope Gosse and then six months as a house surgeon at Amersham, a sector hospital, before joining the army as a lieutenant in the R.A.M.C. in February 1942.

After seven months service in the West Country I was sent with a medical draft on the flag ship of the Union Castle Line, the

Capetown Castle, to India. The Suez Canal was now closed and we sailed in a large convoy round South Africa to Durban, where we spent four nights and were able to stretch our legs ashore after over five weeks at sea. We then sailed on unescorted to Bombay. India and Burma was an experience I would not have missed for anything. My first 9 months was spent in the medical wing of the big British base hospital in Calcutta gaining considerable experience of all branches of medicine; I had 120 beds under my care, and illness accounted for far more casualties than enemy action. I was then posted to Imphal in Manipur State, which adjoined Burma, and which was now occupied by the Japanese. I was responsible for the medical care of all the Army Corps Headquarters staff, which included a great many very senior officers, including the Corps commander, Lt-General Geoffry Scoones, and the brigadier responsible for the medical service of the whole Corps, initially three and in time to number four Divisions. In the middle of March 1944 the Japanese invaded Manipur and we were cut off from all land communications, although we had air superiority. I gained some experience of what it was like to be close to the fighting but never felt that I was in any great danger although on occasion dealing with battle casualties first hand.

At the height of the battle my promotion came through and I was flown out to Chittagong in what is now Bangladesh to take over command of an ambulance train as a major. After six months, in December 1944, I returned to 4 Corps as a staff officer, D.A.D.M.S. – Deputy Assistant Director of Medical Services – for the advance through Burma to Rangoon. By the time we reached Rangoon I had even acquired the use of a two seater plane with an American pilot for my personal use. During my time in India I had also managed two memorable leaves – one in Darjeeling and one trekking through Sikkim and on the Nepalese border.

Unfortunately, I was sensitive to mepacrine, the drug we had to take to avoid getting malaria, and I developed a very severe rash. The battle for Burma had been won and so I flew back to Calcutta and was invalided home and found myself back in Marlborough in December 1945. In March 1946 I was demobilised and then spent six months brushing up my medicine at St Mary's and a further six months as a house surgeon at the Royal Devon and Exeter Hospital and so gained my M.B. B.Chir.

When I joined the family practice in April 1947 my father, Walter, was still not fully retired and continued to see some of his old patients; initially I was not kept as busy as I would have wished. However I did have one week in three on full call for Savernake Hospital where we had to deal with all medical and surgical emergencies in the area. My cousin, Jim, and Dr Wheeler did the other weeks, while Tim concentrated on his midwifery work.

In those days we relied on Salisbury for our pathology work. Dr Darmady came to Savernake twice weekly to collect specimens or where possible to deal with them in the small laboratory at the hospital. A pathologist at Salisbury before the war he had volunteered for the R.A.F. Volunteer Reserve in 1940 and had become interested in the problem presented by kidney failure. In 1945 he constructed a machine using part of the exhaust from a Spitfire aircraft for the central core and cellophane tubing through which the patient's blood could be passed to act as an artificial kidney. This was one of only two machines in the country at the time. He had told me about this machine and it was shortly after I had joined the practice that a very severely injured man who had been involved in a motor accident was brought into Savernake Hospital when I was on call. He had multiple crush injuries and as can happen with such injuries his kidneys began to fail; it was these injuries that Dr Darmady had to deal with in the war that had led to his interest in renal failure and how to combat it. I managed to contact Dr Darmady who was on the Isle of Wight setting up a pathology service there. He travelled up to Marlborough with his machine on a trailer, arriving in the early evening. We connected the patient to the machine and the blood urea, the indicator of his renal failure, was duly lowered as his blood passed through the revolving drum. However, he did not survive the night, his injuries were altogether too severe.

A few days later I had a free day and went to London. I was walking down Bond Street when I met one of the professors from St Mary's Hospital. We had all got to know each other very well during the Blitz and he greeted me saying rather patronisingly, 'Hullo Dick, how are you getting on in general practice?' 'Oh fine,' I replied. 'Mind you, I did have a bit of trouble with the artificial kidney last week.' We were much more advanced in Marlborough than in London!

I started my time in the practice living with my parents in Lloran House but in November 1947 I married Anne Hony; after living in rented property for some eighteen months we purchased our present house in which we have lived since April 1949. My first fifteen months in the practice was the time to prepare for the introduction of the National Health Service. Meetings were held both before and after 5 July 1948 to consider whether Savernake Hospital should have resident doctors, but fears were expressed that it would be difficult to attract suitable residents and the Maurice Wheeler practice continued to provide the day to day care and emergency cover.

The future of the Children's Convalescent Home in the old Union building was also a matter of concern; should it remain under the Wiltshire County Council or be taken over by the Oxford Regional Hospital Board? I had taken over responsibility for medical care in the Home from my father but it had comparatively few children, mostly babies, the result of illicit unions between American G.I.s and the local girls during the war. Authorities from Oxford visited it and interviewed Matron Harral and myself; it was finally decided that it should become a convalescent hospital for children.

Dr Hobson, the visiting consultant physician from Oxford, would arrive at Savernake Hospital in the early afternoon following his picnic lunch in the Forest. He brought with him a new invention, an electrocardiographic machine; it took two people to carry it into the hospital. After his out patient session he did a ward round on which I always accompanied him.

Despite having the benefit of visiting consultants from Oxford and on occasion sending patients over to Oxford, for the most part we had to deal with emergencies ourselves. One of the first of the new consultants to be appointed at Swindon, in November 1950, was Mr J.K. Monro. He had been Professor of Surgery in Singapore and then interned in Changi Gaol. He became an additional consultant for Savernake; furthermore he took up residence in Marlborough. However, we Marlborough G.P.s still had to accept a great deal of responsibilty. We might admit as many as two or three fractured thighs in a week – motor accidents on the A4 were all too frequent in the days before motorways. My own experience as a surgeon was not all that great, but I had been used to dealing with all emergencies at Exeter; the registrar there was not resident and house surgeons in those days had to accept much greater responsibility than they would today. Dr Bashall, the Burbage G.P., was a great help as an anaesthetist; but we often found ourselves giving anaesthetics. Sometimes we might swap ends; I would remove an appendix while Jim gave the anaesthetic and then I would anaesthetise the next patient for him.

Although Swindon had full time consultants, and they could be called on for severe surgical emergencies, it might be difficult at times, especially if Mr Monro was away. I remember once a frantic Nanny arriving at Savernake with a small child who had fallen off a swing; his parents were away for the day. The child had not appeared too bad at first but after two or three hours had lapsed into coma. I realised he must have got a blood clot inside the skull pressing on the brain – far beyond my surgical skills to remove. I rang Swindon in desperation – no consultant was available but I was put on to the surgical registrar. I explained the situation; the resident said he had only once had to open a patient's skull and the patient had died. However, he duly came over to Savernake and we operated. The clot was removed and the child made a full recovery.

Appendicitis was a very common cause for admission and I had performed many appendicectomies. On one occasion I rang up Dr Bashall and asked him if he could come and anaesthetise a man for me who had acute appendicitis. Dr Bashall said he would come straight away. I said, 'There is one slight complication – his appendix has already been removed.' Dr Bashall asked what on earth did I mean and so I explained that the operation had been performed in Ireland and I was sure it could not have been done properly. When I opened him up I found the stump of the appendix had not been invaginated into the caecum and was acutely inflamed – Dr Bashall was impressed by that one.

In 1951 Dr Wheeler's son, Bob, came to join his father who was anxious to retire. He had considerable surgical experience and had gained his Fellowship of the Royal College of Surgeons. His medical experience during the war had been in the Navy. After a years's trial in Marlborough he decided to abandon thoughts of becoming a consultant surgeon; Savernake Hospital gave plenty of opportunity for him to develop his surgical skill. His father moved away and he continued to live in his father's house on the North side of the High Street with his wife and children; he had a small surgery just behind the house. The Maurices were always known by their christian names, as they had been for generations; now Dr Jim, Dr Tim and Dr Dick were joined by Dr Bob – a partnership that was to continue for twenty years without any troubles arising between us.

Meanwhile my work at the Children's Convalescent Hospital was beginning to occupy an increasing amount of my time. Paediatrics was a comparatively new specialty and there were very few paediatricians in the early years after the war. Children were now being sent to Marlborough not just from Swindon but from all over the country; there were not sufficient hospital facilities to care for

'Dr Dick'

children who required long periods confined to bed and a great deal of attention. Although I had been fortunate in gaining quite a lot of medical experience during the war, I had had little experience in treating children's illnesses. The only paediatrician in Oxford at this time was Dr Victoria Smallpeice; she held an out patients at Swindon once a week; and I wrote to her repeatedly asking for help at Marlborough. However, she was never able to come and indeed merely sent me a number of her patients. Fortunately the matron, Mrs Harral, was a real tower of strength and she was splendid with the children and her enthusiasm was infectious. In 1949 I had a letter from Victoria Smallpeice to say a second paediatrician had been appointed at Oxford, Dr Hugh Ellis, he would be doing outpatient clinics and overseeing the inpatients at Swindon. Twice monthly he would come to Marlborough in the afternoons and do an outpatient clinic at Savernake and then see any inpatients both at Savernake and at the Convalescent Hospital. After a couple of years I also had the help of Dr Calnan, a general practitioner from Wroughton, who had considerable knowledge and experience of paediatrics.

Bob Wheeler was a very keen and experienced surgeon and my cousin Jim also had considerable surgical experience and so I was able to give up operating and concentrate on my medical and paediatric work. I still did my week's rota at Savernake dealing with the minor casualties but major surgery I would leave to Bob. Medical admissions all came under my care; both those from our own practice and the many admissions from Ramsbury, Hungerford, Pewsey and Bedwyn. Fortunately, we were on good terms with the local practitioners and it was enjoyable to work with them. I would always accompany the visiting consultant physician on his ward round at Savernake after he had seen the outpatients. Twice monthly on a Monday afternoon I would do an in-patient round at Savernake with Hugh Ellis and then we would go on to the Convalescent Hospital to see any children I had selected for him to see there. He would then come back to supper with Anne and myself, often long after 8 p.m., before returning to Oxford. For my work at the two hospitals I was paid for six 3½ hour sessions.

During the early 'fifties the surgery on the High Street was gradually enlarged, first to accommodate the three Maurice partners and then so that Bob Wheeler could close his surgery and move in too. This was done by extending the surgery into what had been garages, originally stables, and making it into a two story building. By the late fifties an appointment system had been introduced and all our patients, whether private or N.H.S., were encouraged to come to the surgery if possible. Our income was no longer dependent on our private work and it was almost an advantage to us if they were N.H.S. patients rather than seen privately. However, all four partners continued to have some private patients and we might on occasion have to travel 20 or even 30 miles in a day. Further I was responsible for the care of many of the patients in the Froxfield Almshouses, 8 miles from Marlborough, which I had taken over from my father, and Jim had the branch surgery at Avebury. Far fewer people had cars in the 'fifties and 'sixties than today; despite the improved surgery a good deal of time still had to be spent in visiting the sick at home.

Although we did our week on call for Savernake Hospital we remained at all times responsible for the care of our own patients whether we were on call or not. This did have some advantages, we knew the patients and might be able to solve the problem down the telephone; we also knew exactly where the patient lived. I virtually never had to visit Jim's patients in Avebury; Bob made that his responsibility when Jim was away.

My work at the Children's Convalescent Hospital grew steadily during the 'fifties and early 'sixties; it would be true to say it became the predominant interest of my working life. Childrens' illnesses were much more severe and more common than today. Patients with tuberculous meningitis required long periods of inpatient care while they were receiving injections of streptomycin and they had to have weekly lumbar punctures, my responsibility. We had a physiotherapy department and admitted many children suffering from poliomyelitis who required a great deal of rehabilitation. Rheumatic fever accounted for many of our admissions. Caused by the haemolytic streptococcus it frequently affects the heart valves. Although beginning to become less common throughout the country as a whole treatment involved prolonged periods of bed rest and aspirin until blood tests showed it was no longer active; acute hospitals were only too pleased to unload their patients onto us and at least we had a full school now running in the hospital and ward teaching. Nephritis, inflammation of the kidneys, accounted for many of our admissions and also required long periods of bed rest. Bronchiectasis, dilatation and inflammation of the bronchial tubes after whooping cough, also accounted for many of our patients. Parents were encouraged to visit whenever possible. For the most part they could only manage an occasional weekend; Matron Harral was very good with them but I did feel they should also have access to a doctor and so I frequently attended at the hospital on a Saturday or Sunday afternoon. A number of children were admitted with cystic fibrosis, which, in the 'fifties, had a very limited life expectancy. We accepted many children, particularly babies, with congenital abnormalities. Dr Ellis was an enormous help and taught me a great deal. He would bring a party of medical students over from Oxford from time to time to see our patients; they frequently said it was the best afternoon's teaching they had ever had with so many heart murmurs and the like to listen to. In 1953 a fire broke out in a hutted ward, it had been built to serve as a school room before the war, with the nurses accommodation adjoining it; after this a splendid new ward block was constructed and an entirely new nurses home built in a different part of the grounds. One benefit of the N.H.S. was the routine inoculation of children against infectious diseases. These had been accommodated in an isolation hospital adjoining the Union grounds; this was no longer required and the wards were taken over by the Children's Convalescent Hospital for children between the ages of two and seven. In these early years there were between 80 and 100 children in the Convalescent Hospital, and there was always a waiting list.

The Children's Hospital – 'convalescent' was in many ways a misnomer – brought me into contact with a great number of paediatricians from all over the country and I regularly attended meetings of the Oxford Paediatric Society. Paediatrics was now becoming a common specialty and a great deal more thought was given to understanding the problems of children suffering a prolonged illness. There was no paediatrician during my student days at St Mary's; it is difficult to believe it now but parents were not allowed to visit their children in the ward; they could only stand at the door and view them from afar.

Many children we admitted were terminally ill, this was particularly so with babies suffering from congenital defects. Children at this time were accepted only if they were in patients in an acute hospital; they were sent to Marlborough from all over the country and even from Scotland where a consultant regularly sent us his asthma cases; he claimed to have the severest asthmatics and the highest murder rate in the whole of the United Kingdom.

The new Princess Margaret Hospital was fully functioning by 1960 although building work was still in progress; it was not officially opened by Princess Margaret until 1966. Doctor, later Professor, Butler had been appointed paediatrician and had taken over Dr Ellis's duties. He was also made responsible for paediatric care at Salisbury.

In addition he was a co-director of the National Child Development Study, which followed the development of children born in one week in 1958 over a period of many years. After only a few years he moved on to be Professor of Child Health at Bristol and his place was taken by Dr Lilian Jones while Salisbury had its own paediatric consultant. Savernake Hospital still retained some links with Oxford for its consultancy service; a consultant surgeon continued to attend twice monthly for a number of years and Mr Cockin, who had succeeded Mr Scott, provided some orthopaedic cover until his retirement in the late 'eighties, indeed Savernake still has a visiting orthopoedic consultant from Oxford although the Swindon consultants also hold out patient sessions and operate there. A consultant neurologist from Oxford visits the Princess Margaret Hospital and Savernake.

Although there were so many great advances in medicine during the twenty-four years in which the practice was in the hands of the three Maurices and Bob Wheeler the work load of the partners did not seem to alter all that much. However transport for patients in outlying villages became less of a problem; less time was spent visiting patients and more time in the surgery. Routine immunisation of children against infectious diseases also led to less visits being made. The steady development of antibiotics, many of which could be given by mouth, made treatment more effective and less time consuming. Although there were three chemist shops in the town at the start of the N.H.S. the practice has always been allowed to dispense for patients living more than one mile away. After the war placebo mixtures that took some time to make up had virtually ceased to exist; tablets were prescribed much more frequently than medicines. One benefit of the N.H.S. was the financial incentive that allowed practitioners to employ more staff and there was a gradual increase in the number of receptionists employed.

The advances in medicine also led to changes in the Children's Convalescent Hospital. Rheumatic fever, nephritis, poliomyelitis, tuberculous meningitis and bronchiectasis all virtually ceased to exist. Children no longer had to spend long periods in bed. They were now being admitted direct from their homes as well as from hospitals, but only on the recommendation of a consultant. However, the work was still fascinating and could be stressfull. During the early 'sixties asthma was becoming an increasing problem and accounted for many of our admissions; many children were dying from asthma. We still had a waiting list and some deaths even occurred amongst children in other hospitals waiting to come to Marlborough. Sadly, three children died in the Convalescent Hospital from acute asthma, in each case I was there within a few minutes of being summoned but the child was dead. At the time it was thought the over use of antispasmodics by inhalation was contributing to the increased death rate. However steroids had now come into use and children with severe asthma were being given increasingly large doses of cortisone by mouth. The glands responsible for making cortisone would then cease to function and as the oral cortisone was reduced there would be no defence against a sudden severe attack. I read in the *British Medical Journal* that a form of cortisone, beclomethasone diproprionate, that could be administered through an inhaler and have a direct effect on the lungs, was being developed. It had not yet been released for general use but was only undergoing trial. However I wrote to the manufacturer's medical officer and they sent me a large box of the stuff to try. I then wrote to all the consultants who had referred their asthmatic children to Marlborough and asked if I might try out this new inhaler. This produced an angry letter from the allergist at St Mary's Hospital, whom I knew well, saying he had been trying to get a supply of the stuff for months, how on earth had I managed it? Becotide as it is now called has been of great benefit to asthmatics.

During the 'seventies the demand for beds in the Children's Hospital gradually fell off. Virtually no children were confined to bed and all but a few who were grossly handicapped could be sent to their homes during the school holidays. Asthma still accounted for many of the admissions, also cystic fibrosis. Antibiotics and physiotherapy have led to many sufferers from this genetically inherited disease living on into full adulthood; some have even qualified as doctors. Diabetes was another common cause for admission when for one reason or another patients could not be cared for in their own homes. Although the nature of the work had altered to a large extent, it still occupied much of my working life until my retirement.

The work at Savernake Hospital remained much the same throughout the working lives of the fifth generation except that the more acute cases would be sent straight to the Princess Margaret Hospital. We no longer had to deal with the acute major accidents. It was also decided toward the end of the 'sixties to close the children's ward at Savernake, any children requiring hospital care being treated in Swindon. Savernake had many new developments during the 'fifties and 'sixties. The hutted out patient department constructed in

Bob Wheeler, Savernake Hospital 1952–1978

1950 was replaced some twenty years later by a fine new out patient department. A physiotherapy hut was constructed in 1952, the maternity labour ward opened in 1955, a nurse training school opened in 1961 and a nurses recreation hall built in 1964.

The great advantage of doing so much hospital work was that we were in continuous contact with the consultants; this was a great benefit both to the four partners and to our patients. In addition during the 'sixties the scheme allowing general practitioners to attend courses for which they were paid was introduced and helped us to keep up to date with all the advances that were being made in medical care. Savernake Hospital and our regular attendance there meant that we could take blood and other specimens to the Hospital and they would be sent on to the Princess Margaret Hospital in the late morning; pathology played a much bigger part than the stethoscope during our time in the partnership.

In March 1971 Jim retired from the practice; it had been agreed among the partners that they would retire at sixty-five. In the same year Dr Hunter, the Marlborough College resident doctor, also retired. Sickness among the College boys was now much less of a problem; the Maurice Wheeler practice was asked to take on the medical care of the school. The population of Marlborough had increased greatly and so two new partners were appointed, Dr Andrew Reekie and Dr Colin Hallward. The latter would have full responsibility for the school. After three years he left the practice and Dr Reekie took over the medical care of the school assisted by the newly appointed partner, Dr Barney Rosedale. After so many years of stability there was now to be a decade of many changes. The surgery was extended further to accommodate the additional partner and later, in 1979, to provide a room for a nurse who had been appointed to assist in the practice.

In January 1977 Tim retired having reached the age of sixty-five, he was succeeded by his elder son, Nicholas, but always known as Nick. Having previously had a Dr Jim and a Dr Tim we now had a Dr Dick and a Dr Nick. His very first patient in his first surgery said, 'Your great grandfather brought me into the world, your grandfather looked after me in my boyhood and early manhood, your father has looked after me in my middle and old age, I want you into see me into my grave': a wish that was duly fulfilled.

The following year, 1978, the practice suffered a devastating blow when Bob Wheeler developed cancer and died after a short illness in August. At this time a great deal of surgery was still being carried out at Savernake Hospital and a new surgical partner was appointed, Dr Tony Ward F.R.C.S. I retired at the end of 1980 and was duly succeeded by my son, David Pierce, who has the same christian names as his great great grandfather.

The Maurices had traditionally carried out certain public duties and it was mainly Tim who continued in that field. He became a member of the Town Council in 1940 and was Mayor in 1949. When the Kennet District Council was formed in 1973 he joined that and was chairman for four years. He was also a J.P. from 1944 to 1982; he was chairman of the Bench for five years. In 1972 he was given the very rarely bestowed honour of being made a Freeman of the Borough of Marlborough. This honour had also been given to Winston Churchill after the war although he never actually came to Marlborough to collect the accolade. Tim was awarded an O.B.E. for his public duties and was made a Deputy Lieutenant for the County of Wiltshire.

I did have some connection with the boy scouts; I was for a time an Assistant District Commissioner, but decided that I had insufficient time to give to the duties I should be undertaking. I also was appointed a governor of the local secondary modern school and after only a few years found myself first vice chairman and then chairman, an office I held for some fifteen years! I remained a governor of the comprehensive school when that was formed until my retirement on grounds of age.

I am sure that all the Maurices from the fifth generation have found great satisfaction in practising medicine in the town in which they were born. However we could on occasion be brought sharply down to earth. I must have been over fifty when I was sitting in the surgery with an elderly lady in the chair beside my desk. I was being my usual pompous self discussing what treatment would be most appropriate for her arthritis. She suddenly interrupted me – 'Oh, Dr Dick, you were a naughty little boy. I can remember you now, running down the High Street waving your arms and shouting "chuff – chuff – chuff" pretending to be a railway engine with your nanny trotting along behind you, and you used to push us off the pavement.'

We of the fifth generation in Marlborough were particularly fortunate because we lived through a time of such great advances in medicine, from sulphonamides to heart transplants, and having had such a close association with the two Marlborough hospitals and with the visiting consultants.

CHAPTER 7

Epilogue:
The Sixth Generation

It is now some sixteen years since Tim retired and his son, my nephew, Nick, joined the practice. When I retired at the end of 1980 my son, David, succeeded me. Like all the family since my grandfather's time he had trained at St Mary's. He too had done his preclinical work at Cambridge and so he had to go for an interview at Mary's before he could be accepted for a place there. Early in the interview he was asked the usual question, 'Why do you wish to become a doctor, Mr Maurice?' David scratched his head and replied, 'I don't know, my mum always says that no Maurice can think of anything else to do.' Whereupon the Dean sat up and said, 'Good Lord, are you one of the Marlborough Maurices? How's Nick?' No problem after that.

I do not propose to write at length about the sixth generation in Marlborough. Certainly it is a very different world to that which I left over twelve years ago. In 1981 the official name of the practice was still 'Maurice Wheeler' despite Bob Wheeler having died some 2½ years before. Some time after my retirement the name was changed to 'The Marlborough Practice'.

When I retired there were five partners, now there are six whole time and one who works for two-thirds of her time. The first woman practitioner in Marlborough joined the practice in 1984, not a replacement but a much needed additional partner. In 1992 the second woman doctor working part time was appointed.

There is now a big emphasis on primary health care. Fourteen years ago there were only four ancillary staff working in the surgery During the 1980s there was a steady increase in the numbers employed by the practice and in 1989 an entirely new purpose built surgery was constructed on the south side of the river Kennet by George Lane. It stands on land originally owned by the family but had been sold off after Walter's death. There are now eighteen employees in the surgery, although most are not working there full time. They include the practice manager, 4 practice nurses and a nurse practitioner, 5 receptionists, 3 secretaries, 3 pharmacy staff (the practice still supplies medicines and tablets to those living more than one mile away), and a counsellor. The surgery has a well equipped minor operating theatre and now many procedures such as suturing of cuts and other minor surgical procedures are carried out in the surgery rather than being done in Savernake Hospital. The appointment of a nurse practitioner has led to a number of consultations being managed by her with doctor back-up, she is able to relieve some of the pressure on the receptionist staff when urgent appointments are requested. Also in the building attached to the practice are two health visitors, a speech therapist, 6 district nurses, a school nurse and a 'Prospect' nurse for counselling the terminally ill and on occasion the bereaved.

In 1990 a new contract was instituted for general practitioners, the Family Practice Council was replaced by the Family Health Services Authority. This has led to the institution of Health Promotion Clinics. The Marlborough Practice runs diabetic, stop-smoking, hypertension, 'look after your heart', and asthma clinics. There is also a psychiatric nurse who holds stress clinics. Some 900 appointments are made weekly for patients to see a doctor and in addition the nurses see 250 patients each week. The surgery is to be further enlarged and a physiotherapist will be added to the staff.

A computer system was first introduced into the practice in 1989. It is now fully computerised which means that patients requiring follow-ups can no longer slip through the net.

The other big change in the last twelve years has been in the amount of hospital work carried out by the practice. There are now some fifty-three beds at Savernake for in-patient care but this includes a number of beds for the rehabilitation of geriatric cases. The operating theatre has been fully updated but is used only for day surgery, any surgical patients requiring overnight stays now have to go to Swindon. Obstetric work ceased at Savernake in the mid-eighties; it is now carried out only in the Princess Margaret Hospital. The practice do still play their part in the casualty department but this is no longer open at night and far more work is now carried out either in the Marlborough surgery or sent straight to Swindon. Savernake is now a community hospital and is open to all the local general practitioners to care for their patients there when a bed is available.

The Children's Convalescent Hospital has now ceased to exist as

Nick, who succeeded his father, 'Dr Tim', in the practice

David, who succeeded his father, 'Dr Dick', in the practice

such although at the time of writing it does still accommodate children needing psychiatric care.

Although one of the partners has overall responsibility for the care of the pupils at Marlborough College he is assisted by two other members of the practice. The school is now fully co-educational and so one of the assistants is a woman.

On 1 April 1994 the Marlborough Practice became fully fund-holding: this means the practice is now responsible for managing a budget to purchase some hospital and community care, X-ray and pathology investigations, and the cost of prescribed drugs.

I cannot be sure of this, but I very much doubt if the two Maurices today travel as many miles in their cars visiting their patients as Thelwall had to on horseback 200 years ago.

Index

Illustration references are given in *italics*.

Index